Stranger than Fiction

Weird Stories and Ghostly Happenings

D1516174

Stranger than Fiction

Weird Stories and Ghostly Happenings

Martin Walsh

Cover Design by Dennis Barnett

SCHOLASTIC INC.

New York Toronto London Auckland Sydney

No part of this publication may be reproduced in whole or in part, or stored in a retrieval system, or transmitted in any form or by any means, electronic, mechanical, photocopying, recording, or otherwise, without written permission of the publisher. For information regarding permission, write to Scholastic Inc., 730 Broadway, New York, NY 10003.

ISBN 0-590-41574-3

12 11 10 9 8 7 6 5 4 3 2   0 1 2/9

Printed in the U.S.A.   01

CONTENTS

THE SEARCH FOR ATLANTIS

The search for Atlantis, one of the world's oldest unsolved mysteries, may be nearing an end. For over 2,000 years the name Atlantis has intrigued mankind. But it was not until recent years that any clues to the disappearance of the supposed lost continent were ever found. Indeed the very idea of a lost Atlantis bordered on the fantastic as far as most experts were concerned. However a remarkable discovery may hold the key to the long sought continent. The discovery and the subsequent theories explaining the disappearance of Atlantis are more exciting than any mystery story. It is now possible that soon we will know the truth about Atlantis.

The legend of Atlantis, the mysterious and beautiful lost continent that disappeared beneath the sea, has fascinated man for thousands of years. Countless books have been devoted to the subject. Scientific expeditions have searched in vain in every corner of the world for the elusive Atlantis. Fantastic theories have placed Atlantis in virtually every part of the earth. Despite the research, it began to appear that the theory of a lost continent submerged beneath the sea was nothing more than a yearning in man's mind for a better world than his own. No definite evidence had been produced that proved Atlantis' existence. It seemed possible that the legend of Atlantis was going to be just an unsupported and unsolved mystery.

But somehow the legend refused to die. Atlantis represented a gap in man's knowledge that somehow had to be explained. Then dramatically, after over 2,000 years of searching, scientists made some fascinating discoveries that may prove that Atlantis actually once existed in the Aegean Sea, south of Greece.

The legend of Atlantis had its beginnings with the writings of Plato, the famous Greek philosopher who lived about 427-347 B.C. He described Atlantis in glowing detail. Basing his writings on stories told by Egyptian priests, Plato described Atlantis as being a large continent to the west of the Gates of Hercules, or what is now known as the Rock of Gibraltar.

Plato described Atlantis as a beautiful land inhabited by a noble race of people. The people had formed a perfect form of government and lived in harmony.

Then slowly, according to Plato, the people began to fall into a state of moral decay. As they became more corrupt, the gods decided to punish them for their weaknesses. Plato then describes how Zeus, the ruler of the gods, assembled the other gods to discuss just what punishment Atlantis should receive. Plato wrote, "And when he had assembled them he spoke thus . . ."

Here Plato's writings stop and were never completed, and here the mystery of Atlantis begins. No one knows why Plato never completed his discussion of Atlantis. Future historians viewed Plato's Atlantis in various ways. Most felt that his description of Atlantis was only symbolic in nature; that Atlantis represents a yearning in man for a fertile place without disease and care. Others felt that Plato was describing a true island paradise that once actually existed.

For over 2,000 years since the time of Plato, the search for Atlantis has continued. Probably no other mystery has caused such discussion. But it was not until 1956 that the first big break came in the Atlantis mystery. This discovery and several succeeding ones were breakthroughs that may at last prove that the existence of Atlantis was a reality.

Seismologist Angelos Galanopoulos of the University of Greece had devoted almost his entire life to exploring the islands of the Mediterranean and Aegean Seas. In 1956, on the island of Santorini which is north of Crete in the Aegean, Galanopoulos was exploring a mine shaft. Penetrating into the deepest part of the shaft, he was startled to find the fire-blackened ruins of a stone house. Inside, Professor Galanopoulos discovered the teeth of a man and woman. The Professor was further startled to discover that radio-carbon analysis of the teeth indicated that the man and woman had died in 1400 B.C. Furthermore, the remains were covered by over 100 feet of volcanic ash, indicating that a violent volcanic eruption had occurred on Santorini in the 15th century B.C.

Professor Galanopoulos' discovery, and other evidence that he had gathered through painstaking research, slowly began to fit into a pattern. Galanopoulos proposed a theory that Santorini was actually the site of the legendary Atlantis. He reasoned that Plato had erred in his placing of Atlantis in the Atlantic Ocean. Professor Galanopoulos was convinced that a violent earthquake had destroyed Atlantis and that soon his theories would prove correct.

Fascinated by Professor Galanopoulos' discovery, an American-Greek team of scientists, headed by James Mavor of the Woods Hole Oceanographic Institute in Massachusetts, organized an expedition. Sailing in the research ship *Chain*, Mavor discovered through the use of sonar that the islands in the Santorini region had once been part of a larger land mass. Seismic profiles further indicated that the region resembled in close detail the description of Atlantis given by Plato.

Landing on Santorini the team began digging

at a vineyard site just south of the village of Akratiri. Then an old peasant from the village led the team to a small cave hollowed out of the white ash cliffs. The peasant had become curious when his donkey stepped on the floor of the cave causing some of the floor to collapse.

Curiosity, a trait of every good scientist, caused the researchers to follow the peasant to the cave. Peering into the opening caused by the donkey's weight, they were startled to discover below a perfectly preserved room.

In a few days the diggers had unearthed an ancient city completely intact, unharmed by the passing years. Two and three story buildings were still standing just as they had once stood thousands of years before. Further exploration revealed vases, oil lamps, mortars and pestles, and thousands of other artifacts.

On the walls of many of the houses were beautiful frescoes. Just as in the city of Pompeii, in Italy, the city beneath Akratiri was perfectly preserved in time by a thick covering of volcanic ash and pumice.

But there was one important difference between Pompeii and Akratiri. Both cities had obviously been struck by a violent eruption, but in all their digging at Akratiri James Mavor and his team were unable to find any human remains, although they did find the remains of dogs, sheep, and pigs. Furthermore they were unable to find any gold, silver, or other valuable objects. This could only mean one thing. The people of Akratiri, as opposed to Pompeii, had plenty of advance warning that disaster was going to strike. Obviously they had departed, leaving the city just as it was found by James Mavor and his team.

Radio-carbon analysis of the site indicated that the city had been destroyed in the 15th century B.C. This date matches the discoveries made by Professor Galanopoulos and has led scientists to estimate that the volcanic explosion that covered Akratiri with over 100 feet of ash must have been the most violent explosion ever known to man.

Just how violent was this explosion? In modern times we have had the eruption of a volcano on the island of Krakatoa in the Pacific Ocean to show us how powerful a volcanic explosion can be. The Krakatoa eruption in 1883 blew the top off the 1,460 foot high island, sending a column of flames over 30 miles into the air, hurling rocks over 50 miles through the air, and sending tidal waves circling the Earth, destroying millions of dollars in property and killing thousands. Close to 300 entire towns were destroyed by the eruption and an estimated 36,000 people were killed.

Java, a nearby island, was struck with waves 118 feet high, while on the island of Sumatra the waves reached a height of 131 feet.

The Krakatoa explosion was so loud that it was heard 2,250 miles to the southeast in Australia, and 2,968 miles to the west in the Indian Ocean island of Rodriquez. The sound waves traveled three times around the Earth.

The world has seldom witnessed the power unleashed at Krakatoa. It was powerful enough so that when the explosions subsided and the waves receded a Dutch warship was found on Sumatra, stranded half a mile inland and 30 feet above sea level.

In the United States fire engines were called in many western cities. Citizens were alarmed at the fiery red color of the sky, certain that something was burning.

But as powerful and destructive as the Krakatoa explosion was, it was small compared to that of Santorini. Krakatoa deposited only one foot of volcanic ash on nearby islands. Santorini deposited up to 100 feet.

Inhabitants of Santorini and nearby islands such as Crete had no doubt been aware that the 4,900-foot mountain was going to explode. This is evidenced by the absence of human remains in Akratiri. But no one knows just how far the refugees actually got, although an interesting theory has been advanced.

Santorini exploded with a blast estimated to be the equal of several hundred hydrogen bombs. Through research, scientists have been able to reconstruct much of what must have happened. First, tremendous quantities of pumice were violently thrown from the crater, covering the surrounding sea. Then the entire mountain exploded, casting great boulders in all directions. The roof of the mountain and portions of the surrounding walls then collapsed into the bottom of the gigantic cavity caused by the explosion.

This caused a violent recoil as the hot ash mixed with the cold water. Waves of tremendous height rushed forth from the island traveling at 200 miles per hour. The waves, estimated to be almost 700 feet high in the beginning, smashed into the island of Crete destroying the many towns and cities of the island. The island of Anaphir, only 15 miles from Santorini, was struck with tremendous force, covering the island with layers of ash 530 feet thick.

The immense waves then continued on their way, destroying everything in their path. Eventually they smashed into the coast of Egypt, causing extensive damage. Such was the force of the waves that the ancient port of Ugarit, Syria, was covered by water. Ugarit was 640 miles from Santorini.

Today, remains of the explosion still cover the floor of the Aegean and Mediterranean — over an 80,000 square mile area. A layer of volcanic ash, from several inches to several feet thick, remains on the seabed floor as a grim reminder of the power of nature.

What happened to the inhabitants of Santorini, Crete, and the other islands of the Aegean? Beyond doubt most of the people of Santorini managed to escape. However, many merely moved to nearby islands and were probably killed in the eruption. Some managed to escape and what happened to the survivors is a fascinating story in itself.

Probably a few survivors managed to climb

the highest mountains and escape the effects of the explosion and the flood. These survivors, as well as some who may have been away from the islands at the time, somehow made their way to the mainland, the area today known as Greece. Greece at this time was inhabited by many groups of primitive tribes.

The Santorini survivors, highly cultured, possessed of the ability to work bronze and gold, and with knowledge of government and law, then started a new civilization on the shores of Greece. This civilization grew and flourished into one of the greatest the world has ever known, that of ancient Greece.

Beyond doubt, the great civilization that prospered on the islands of the Aegean Sea lived on in the memories of the survivors and in Greek legends. Perhaps Plato's description of Atlantis was a description of an actual city on the island of Santorini.

Investigations by scientists such as Professor Galanopoulos and James Mavor certainly indicate that the riddle of Atlantis may be close to a solution. Was Santorini the beautiful island kingdom of Atlantis? Will the city uncovered at Akratiri prove to be the capital city described in Plato's writings?

Today plans are underway for the construction of an underground museum at Akratiri. Archaeologists hope to preserve the ancient city exactly as it was found. In this way the city will be protected from the elements by a canopy of earth.

Experts are convinced that the excavations at Akratiri will rival those of Pompeii.

Many questions have yet to be answered. Will the remains of the buried city of Akratiri finish the 2,000-year-old search for Atlantis once and for all? But then perhaps the story of Atlantis will always remain the way Plato left it — unfinished.

BIGFOOT

The Abominable Snowman is a large hairy beast with an apelike body and a face that resembles a man's. The creature has been sighted by local tribesmen in the mountainous regions of central Asia. From time to time reports concerning the Abominable Snowman have appeared in the papers. The reports have aroused the interest of scientists and explorers. Several expeditions have been organized into the area, but so far no definite proof of the existence of the Abominable Snowman has turned up. Despite this fact, many people are convinced that such a creature actually exists in central Asia.

Overlooked in all the interest in the Asian Abominable Snowman is the possibility that the United States and Canada may possess an Abominable Snowman of their own. Recently an amazing discovery by two young men brought to light an old legend concerning the existence of "Bigfoot," a creature that is remarkably similar to the Abominable Snowman of Asia. Does such a creature exist in the wilderness region of the western United States and Canada?

For more than 100 years, strange stories have been coming from the mountain ranges of the western United States and Canada. These stories tell of a half-man, half-animal creature that lives in this vast wilderness.

Incredible stories of a huge seven-foot-tall hairy giant that walks on two legs just like a man have circulated throughout the mining camps and small towns of the Pacific Northwest. Terrified hunters and trappers have told of being attacked by such a creature which soon came to be called "Bigfoot."

Yet for 100 years these stories remained in the realm of fantasy and superstition. The legend of Bigfoot was scoffed at except by those who had direct experience with the creature. Skeptics pointed out that not a single solid piece of evidence had ever been exhibited. Not a single bone or footprint of the creature had ever been found.

Then one day in 1967 two young men obsessed with the idea of either proving or disproving the existence of Bigfoot set forth on a journey. When these two men returned to civilization from the rugged forest region they had the proof they needed. These two men could prove that there was a half-man, half-animal creature in the woods. Now the world would believe—or would it?

Roger Patterson and Bob Gimlin were determined to prove that there was truth to the legend of Bigfoot. Roger Patterson was a 34-year-old rancher from Yakima, Washington. When he was a very young man Patterson read an article in a magazine telling of the possible existence of Bigfoot. The article reported instances of various sightings of the creature by reliable individuals in several states and Canada. From that moment Roger Patterson decided he would be the one to track down Bigfoot and prove that the creature really existed.

Bob Gimlin was an experienced animal tracker who had tracked the largest animals known to man. These two men hoped to work together in search of Bigfoot.

Word had reached the men that fresh tracks made by a giant creature had been found in the area of Bluff Creek in northern California. This was an area of thick forests on the western slope of the Cascade Mountains. It is one of the most rugged areas in the United States, and very few persons have ever set foot in these woods. In fact much of the mountain region has not even been fully mapped.

Patterson and Gimlin made their way into the deep woods. On horseback they moved slowly up the winding Bluff Creek. Thick vegetation covered the ground and trees over 200 feet high cast long shadows.

Floods had washed out the creek a few years back. The rampaging waters had knocked over trees, making the progress of the two men even slower. As the vegetation thickened the men had to dismount and lead their horses through the underbrush.

As the men fought their way into the thick woods their minds wandered to thoughts of Bigfoot. What would happen if and when they faced the creature? Would he attack them, or was Bigfoot merely the product of the imagination, as so many people had told them before they started on their journey? Just who or what was Bigfoot?

Patterson and Gimlin were not the kind to be afraid of anything. But there was a strange silence to the woods as the men left behind all traces of civilization. Tracking down a bear was one thing, but Bigfoot was something different. There was no doubt that a creature like Bigfoot might have the power to think and reason just as they did. Perhaps Bigfoot was watching their every step even now.

Patterson and Gimlin were coming to a bend in the creek. A large stump overturned by the flood blocked their view ahead. Then it happened!

Suddenly the horses reared into the air and snorted. Then horses and riders fell to the ground in a tangle. Working quickly, Patterson, an experienced horseman, freed himself. Then he saw what had caused the horses to panic.

In front of the two men, about 125 feet across the creek, was the creature. There was no doubt about it. It was Bigfoot! The creature's head was very human, although its forehead was much longer and more slanting. It had a humanlike nose with white nostrils. Its arms hung almost to its knees when it walked. Its hair was two to four inches long, brown underneath but brighter at the top.

All of this Patterson noticed at a glance, quickly registering in his mind the many details that he would write down when there was time. As he stared the creature began to move; it walked on two legs. It had hands and feet much like a man's, but was much larger than any man. There was little doubt that the creature was over seven feet tall and looked like it weighed from 300 to 350 pounds.

Slowly, cautiously, without taking his eyes from the creature, Patterson reached into his saddlebag. He pulled out his camera, loaded with color film and ready to shoot.

As Bigfoot slowly began to move away, Patterson inched closer. But then the creature, apparently alarmed at Patterson's presence, began to move more rapidly. Patterson began running after the creature, pointing his camera at Bigfoot. Then a strange thing happened.

All of a sudden the creature just stopped in its tracks and stared at Patterson. It seemed spellbound by the whirring of the movie camera. Patterson stopped, not moving a muscle. All the while he kept the camera pointed at Bigfoot, hardly daring to even breathe.

Then the creature, apparently growing tired of the camera, began running again. Patterson, still pointing his camera, intent on getting as much film footage as possible, ran after it. Through the underbrush he crashed, pushing back the bushes that were scratching his face and hands.

Bob Gimlin by this time had settled down the horses and joined in the chase. Bigfoot seemed confused by the entire chain of events. As it ran it glanced back at the men as if wondering at this intrusion of its wilderness kingdom. Soon the creature picked up speed and the men were left far behind.

For three and a half miles Roger Patterson and Bob Gimlin trailed Bigfoot. Then they lost its tracks; Bigfoot was gone.

The men returned to the place where they had first sighted Bigfoot. They took plaster casts of the creature's tracks. The men noticed with amazement that its footprints proved that Bigfoot must weigh over 300 pounds. The length of its stride showed that it must be at least seven feet tall.

When Patterson and Gimlin returned to civilization the first thing that they did was to make sure that their film was processed carefully. Their next step was to take the film to a large Hollywood motion picture company. Hard-bitten movie experts adept at any kind of makeup were amazed at the film. They were positive that the creature was not an ape or large bear. They were even more certain that the amazing film showed a creature that they had never seen before.

But everyone else was not as sure as the movie experts. Soon news of the film and the plaster cast footprints began to appear in newspapers and magazines. Many insisted that the two young men had never actually seen anything in the wilderness. That the "Bigfoot" that they claimed to have filmed was nothing but a "man in a bear suit." Many claimed that the whole thing was nothing but a big hoax maneuvered by Patterson and Gimlin as part of a get-rich-quick plan.

Finally Patterson and Gimlin showed their film to a group of well-known scientists. The scientists studied the film over and over again. Some were convinced, others were not.

The pictures looked real enough. But why, questioned the scientists, had so little evidence been found over the years? Why had not a single bone ever been located?

The answer to this was easy, all of the scientists knew perfectly well. Nature quickly does away with the remains of animals that die in the woods. Even the remains of the largest animals disappear because they are devoured by woodland scavengers.

But why had so few people seen Bigfoot? A trip into the forests of western United States and

Canada could give the answer to this question. Patterson and Gimlin found the going almost impossible. Few men have ever been in the region. As a result few men have really had the chance to see Bigfoot.

But the real answer may be found in the actions of Bigfoot when Patterson and Gimlin discovered him. The first thing the creature did was turn and run. Perhaps through bitter experience Bigfoot knows the ways of man and wishes to have nothing to do with him. As man gradually moves closer perhaps Bigfoot moves further and further into the deepest parts of the wilderness.

On the other hand perhaps Bigfoot does not exist at all, as many claim. The pictures taken by Roger Patterson may have been only a clever hoax after all.

But Roger Patterson and Bob Gimlin know that deep in the northern woods Bigfoot is waiting. Soon they plan on returning to the place where they saw and photographed the creature. This time there will be many more men on the trip, each with a specific assignment. Each man will carry a camera. Each man will also carry a special gun. These guns will not be used to kill Bigfoot, but will only tranquilize him so that he can be brought back for the entire world to see.

Then and only then will the doubters be convinced, and the world will know for sure if Roger Patterson and Bob Gimlin were telling the truth. Only then will the mystery of Bigfoot be solved.

VISITORS FROM THE SKIES

Do you believe in flying saucers? Exeter, New Hampshire, is a quiet little town in New England. It is far removed from the busy life of the city. But on the night of September 3, 1965, tiny Exeter became the center of a sensational news story. It all began on a dark, lonely road outside the town.

A deserted highway was no place for a young man to be walking alone at two o'clock in the morning, and 18-year-old Norman Muscarello knew it. Muscarello was nervous. He hadn't seen a car for some time, and his hopes of ever getting a ride were getting slimmer with each passing minute. Muscarello was hitchhiking along Route

150 headed toward his hometown of Exeter, New Hampshire.

Norman was coming from visiting a friend in Amesbury, Massachusetts. He had sold his car because in a few weeks he would be going into the Navy. At the moment Norman would have given anything to have his old car back.

Muscarello was now only a few miles from Exeter. The stillness of the night seemed strange to him, even though he had walked along Route 150 many times. Muscarello's senses were alerted, as he strained his ears and eyes for any possible sign of danger. The silence was almost oppressive, and before he knew it Muscarello had quickened his steps. A strange feeling which he couldn't explain even to himself seemed to grip him.

Muscarello was now walking past an empty field. He could see two farmhouses in the distance. Then it happened!

As Muscarello stared in amazement, suddenly from between the two houses he saw something that he would never forget. A huge round object glowing brightly with red pulsating lights came from the sky. The object headed straight for Muscarello. Norman couldn't believe his eyes. He began scrambling along the highway, running for his life. The "thing" seemed to grow larger and kept coming toward him. As Muscarello stumbled along the dark highway, he glanced over his shoulder at the glowing object. It appeared to be coming straight for him and in a few minutes would surely crush him.

There was only one thing to do. Muscarello

dived into the soft shoulder of the road. He rolled over and over. Finally he came to rest against a brick wall. Then he looked up.

The thing was directly over him. It was illuminating the entire countryside. It just seemed to hang there staring at him, waiting for him to make a move.

Then the object backed off slowly. Gradually it moved over the roof of one of the houses across the field. Then it disappeared into the night.

Muscarello was panic-stricken. He rose from the ditch and scrambled wildly across the field toward the farmhouse. He pounded on the front door, screaming wildly. No one answered.

Muscarello ran back toward Route 150. As he ran he glanced back over his shoulder. But there was no sign of the "thing."

Luckily Muscarello reached the highway just as a car was coming. He waved his arms and the car stopped. A middle-aged couple took him into Exeter.

In Exeter, Muscarello headed straight for the police station.

Officer Reginald "Scratch" Toland had never seen anyone in quite the same condition as Norman Muscarello in all his years on the Exeter police force. By this time Muscarello was in a state of near shock. His face was white and he was trembling and could barely speak.

Slowly Officer Toland managed to piece together the fantastic story that Muscarello told him. Toland found it hard to believe Muscarello's strange tale. But still he had no doubt that the young man had seen something. What it could have been, Officer Toland was not sure.

Muscarello pleaded with Officer Toland to go with him to the place where he had seen the object.

At that moment Officer Eugene "Gene" Bertrand pulled into the station. Bertrand had been on night patrol. An hour earlier he had come across a woman. The woman was sitting alone by the side of Route 101. The woman was shaking nervously as she told Bertrand a strange story. She told of how an object had been following her in the skies for over twelve miles. The object had brilliant flashing red lights. It was completely silent. Finally the woman had pulled to the side of the road. The object seemed to hover over her. Then it turned and disappeared with tremendous speed into the night.

"I thought she was a kook, so I didn't even bother to radio in," said Bertrand.

Scratch Toland and Norman Muscarello had been listening eagerly to Officer Bertrand's story.

"This sound like the thing you saw?" asked Toland, looking at Muscarello.

"Sounds exactly like it," he replied. "Look," the boy said desperately, "I know you don't believe me. I don't blame you. But you've got to send somebody back out there with me."

Officer Gene Bertrand was puzzled. The woman sitting by the side of the road and now this young man . . . Bertrand wasn't the kind to be easily shaken. He was an Air Force veteran. He had been a pilot during the Korean War. On the Exeter police force, Bertrand was the one they always sent for in the toughest spots.

But now as Gene Bertrand and Norman Muscarello sped along in the patrol car toward the place where Muscarello had seen the thing come out of the sky, Bertrand wondered. Tales of strange flying objects had been coming in regularly to the Exeter police station. But Bertrand was doubtful. He had heard and read many stories about flying saucers. He knew about the various reports of Unidentified Flying Objects (UFOs) from all over the world. Somehow Gene Bertrand believed that there was an explanation for all of these flying objects. Yet still he couldn't help but wonder.

The patrol car had now reached the open field where Muscarello had seen the object. It was three in the morning. Nothing was in sight. The night was very dark and strangely quiet. Bertrand and Muscarello stood by the cruiser. Muscarello was extremely tense, his eyes scanning the darkness in all directions. Despite their state of alertness, the two could hear or see nothing.

Bertrand called to Scratch Toland on the police radio. He told Toland that they were going to investigate.

Bertrand and Muscarello began walking across the deserted field. They headed in the direction of the farmhouse. Bertrand took out his flashlight. The light pierced the darkness. But still the two could see nothing.

They were now approaching a split-rail fence.

Suddenly, mysteriously, strange sounds came from the nearby farm. The horses began to whinny and kick. The dogs began to howl. The animals could sense something that Bertrand and Muscarello couldn't.

Without warning the boy shouted, "I see it! I see it!"

Bertrand's back had been turned to the boy. He wheeled around and stared. Bertrand couldn't believe his eyes. From behind the tall pine trees in the distance, a brilliant glowing round object came toward them!

Bertrand was blinded by the light. The object seemed to be twice as large as the nearby farmhouse. The thing didn't make a sound. Bertrand could see a row of red lights circling the object that seemed to glow brightly and then dim again. The entire countryside was bathed in red, the color of blood. The white farmhouse seemed to glow in the darkness. Even the other farmhouse one hundred yards away could be seen plainly.

The thing was moving in a weird fluttering sort of way. Bertrand looked at Muscarello. The boy was frozen in his tracks. Bertrand grabbed him as they began to race across the field as fast as their legs could carry them. The thing was motionless in the air above them. All the while they could hear the noises of the horses and dogs coming from the farm.

Bertrand reached the patrol car. "My God, I see the thing myself!" he shouted into the police radio.

Bertrand and Muscarello were now joined by

Officer David Hunt. Hunt had heard everything on his police radio. He had listened to the conversation between Bertrand and Toland and had raced to the scene.

The thing was still there. Hunt could see it in the distance. It was now motionless above the row of trees. It seemed undecided about what to do. Officers Bertrand, Hunt, and Norman Muscarello stood staring at the fantastic glowing object. Never in their lives would they forget the sight they were now watching.

Then the object began moving across the tops of the trees. It was moving east toward the town of Hampton. Beyond lay the Atlantic Ocean. The three watched as the object passed from their view. The horses stopped their kicking. The dogs no longer barked. Darkness returned to the field. It was all over.

What was it that had passed across the quiet New England countryside? A young man and two experienced police officers certainly had seen something. Were these intelligent beings from another planet? Was this their spaceship? Were the red glowing lights their signal lights? What strange beings peered from within the glowing object?

At this time all of these questions remain a mystery. But one thing is certain. The people of Exeter, New Hampshire, are looking toward the skies. Some of them believe. Do you?

THE MAN WHO LAUGHED
AT DEATH

Harry Houdini died over forty years ago, yet the story of his feats of magic will live forever. Even more incredible as time passes are the stories of Houdini's great escapes. They called him "The Escape King." But there was one day that proved beyond doubt that Harry Houdini was the greatest magician and escape artist who ever lived. Houdini's brush with death, buried in a coffin under ten feet of water, is a story that will make you wonder as the world of his day wondered, "Just what sort of man was the Great Houdini"?

Death was Harry Houdini's constant companion. For 25 long years Harry Houdini cheated death every time he stepped before an audience. Harry Houdini died in 1927, but there are those who believe that the ghost of Houdini is still among us. Houdini couldn't die, they say. He was indestructible. He proved that to the world on August 5, 1926.

Those who gathered around the pool of the Hotel Shelton in New York City on that date will always remember the scene. Harry Houdini, "The Great Houdini," stood next to a large metal coffin. Doctors examined the great magician, checking his heart beat, his pulse, and his blood pressure. They announced that Houdini was ready for the greatest test of his entire life.

Several months before, Houdini had told the world that he would remain inside a coffin longer than any other living man. He further stated that he would perform his act underwater so that there could be no possible trickery. No one had ever dared such an act before.

The doctors carefully checked the coffin. They announced that there was enough air for a man to survive for perhaps three or four minutes. Perhaps if a man used the air sparingly, they said, he could last for ten to fifteen minutes.

Houdini walked slowly toward the casket. As the crowd stared in disbelief, he lowered himself into the metal box. Then the lid was soldered tightly to the casket. Reporters and photographers moved in closer. There could be no doubt. The solid metal casket was now sealed off from all possible means of escape. The crowd settled back in their seats, watching and waiting. The long-awaited moment for the coffin to be lowered was coming.

The world had become used to the impossible from Harry Houdini. He had escaped from everything that man could invent. He had escaped from packing cases thrown into the deepest rivers. He had escaped from burglar-proof safes. Once he had been tied, handcuffed, and placed into a giant milk can filled with water. He was free in seconds. He'd escaped from huge paper bags, blocks of solid ice, and prison cells. In the short space of 25 years Harry Houdini had become a living legend.

Who was this man who amazed the world time after time? What was there in the background of this great man that brought thousands of people to see him every time he performed? Was he a true spirit who had supernatural powers as some said? Or was he an ordinary man with an ordinary background?

The legend of Houdini had begun many years before. Houdini's real name was Ehrich Weiss. He was born in Appleton, Wisconsin, the son of a Jewish rabbi and a Catholic mother.

When Ehrich was only eight years old, an event occurred that changed the course of his life. A traveling circus came to the tiny town of Appleton. Young Ehrich saw the posters and a feeling deep within him told him that he just had to see the circus.

Young Ehrich was captured by the magic of

the circus, but there was one performer that interested Ehrich above all the others. This performer was the magician. Ehrich watched with awe as the magician performed his tricks. From that moment on Ehrich became obsessed with one thought — he would become the greatest magician who ever lived.

Ehrich's father, Dr. Mayer Weiss, shook his head slowly and smiled when young Ehrich announced his plans. He knew the magic of a circus, and he felt that Ehrich would forget all about it in a few days. But Dr. Weiss couldn't see the burning look in his son's eyes. Someday that same look would cast a spell over thousands of people the world over.

At the age of twelve Ehrich Weiss left home and became "Eric the Great." He went from place to place across the country. Sometimes he worked for a traveling circus or a medicine show. Standing as tall as possible he would announce, "I am 'Eric the Great.' I can let anyone tie me with ropes, and I can get free." Just as his father had once done, the audience would smile and shake their heads. But when "Eric" escaped from his ropes they were amazed that a 12-year-old could perform such a feat.

Once when "Eric the Great" was performing with a small circus he decided to make his act more interesting. He invited the town sheriff to tie him up. The sheriff stepped forward and tied Eric. The boy magician escaped in a few minutes.

The sheriff's face grew red with anger. The young boy was making a fool out of him. Suddenly the sheriff took out a pair of handcuffs. "Here, you're such a smart youngster. Let's see you get out of these!"

"I'll try," Eric said slowly, "but not in front of everyone." The crowd laughed in ridicule. Now it was the sheriff's turn to show up the young magician.

Eric stepped behind a curtain. In a few minutes he stepped out again. In one hand he held up a pair of handcuffs. The legend of Houdini was born.

Eric wandered through the West. When he wasn't working, he practiced. His skill grew and grew but there weren't many circuses looking for a 12-year-old magician. The time between jobs became longer and longer, and often Eric didn't eat for days at a time. Finally he learned that his family had moved to New York City. There he joined them.

For a while Eric worked in a factory as a tie cutter, but a regular job was not for the restless young man. He continued his tricks of magic whenever anyone would hire him. Often he worked in dark noisy beer halls, or even on street corners.

This was the age of vaudeville. It was the period before motion pictures, radio, and television, when people enjoyed live stage entertainment performed by traveling bands of entertainers. It was an era that was just perfect for a performer like Ehrich Weiss, or "The Great

Houdini" as he now called himself. But try as he could, Houdini couldn't seem to reach the big time. He couldn't seem to advance beyond the dingy beer halls and tiny dime museums.

For a while things brightened up for Houdini. At the age of 20 he met Beatrice "Bessie" Rahner. They fell in love immediately and were married in Coney Island after a day on the "death defying" rides of the famous amusement park.

Life for Houdini and Bessie didn't improve. Bessie became Houdini's assistant and traveled with him all over the country. She suffered hunger and despair along with her husband. Things reached rock bottom one night in Nova Scotia. The two were completely broke and were without food or shelter. That night they were forced to sleep on a cold doorstep.

Houdini never lost his hope however. Somehow he knew that he was destined for greatness. For him it was just a matter of time. "I can do it because I am the Great Houdini," he would say.

Finally Houdini made a bold move that changed his career. He decided to go to Europe and try his luck. Borrowing the money from friends, he arrived in England without a job.

Houdini knew that he had to act boldly. It was either that or starve. Shortly after arriving in England, Houdini walked into Scotland Yard, the home of the famous British police. Houdini strode straight into Superintendent Melville's office and challenged Melville to handcuff him with the best pair of handcuffs in Scotland Yard.

The Superintendent laughed at Houdini.

"Look, young man, if we put handcuffs on you they will be real ones. I can assure you that you won't get loose either."

"Go ahead, handcuff me. Put on three pairs, four pairs, as many as you want. Put a pair of leg irons on me too," replied Houdini.

Melville took a pair of handcuffs from his desk. He marched Houdini into the hallway, placed Houdini's arms around a large pillar, and handcuffed him to the pillar. "That's how we fasten Yankee criminals who come over here and get into trouble," Melville said. "We'll come back and get you loose in a couple of hours," laughed Melville.

"Wait!" called Houdini before Melville had taken a dozen steps. "Wait and I'll go with you." With that Houdini stepped away from the pillar and the cuffs fell noisily to the floor. Melville stared. He couldn't believe his eyes.

News of Houdini's escape from Scotland Yard spread like wildfire. Soon every theater in England was asking for the Great Houdini. He was an overnight sensation.

From that time on there was no stopping Houdini. He toured England and Scotland. In each town Houdini issued a challenge to anyone to try to keep him prisoner in any way that they could invent. He escaped from straitjackets and safes. Often he was tied and suspended by rope from the top of a high building. He always escaped.

The legend of Houdini was now becoming

worldwide. No one had ever contained "The Escape King" or "The Handcuff King," as many called him. With each incredible escape the world began to wonder. What sort of man was this Houdini? The stories of his escapes made many people wonder if Houdini was an ordinary flesh and blood person. There were those who came to believe that Houdini escaped by supernatural means. No ordinary mortal could perform the escapes that Houdini did, they speculated.

There were even some who believed that Houdini was a true spirit living in our midst. Houdini, they said, would allow himself to be locked and handcuffed in a packing case. He would then transform his body into a spiritual state. The spirit would then pass through the packing case. Then Houdini would change himself back into his human form and appear on the outside of the case.

Even such a man as Sir Arthur Conan Doyle was convinced that Houdini was possessed of supernatural powers. Doyle, creator of the famous Sherlock Holmes mystery stories, became interested in spiritualism toward the end of his life. Doyle thought that even Houdini himself wasn't aware of the extraordinary powers that he had.

Indeed there seemed to be no other explanation for Houdini's escape acts and tricks of magic. People were amazed as he made an elephant disappear on the stage right before their eyes, or appeared to walk right through a solid brick wall. As the legend of Houdini grew and grew, the belief that he was a spirit became stronger. The deep, serious, almost hypnotic look in his eyes made even those who knew him wonder.

This was the man who had brought so many to the poolside of the Shelton Hotel in 1926. No man could have drawn such a crowd except the Great Houdini. Houdini was 52 years old at the time, and some said that he was past his peak as a performer. He was a man possessed with a tremendous ego, and he had heard the remarks. He aimed to make this the most spectacular act of his entire career, in order to dispel any notions that he was slowing up.

In the summer of 1926 New York had been amazed by the performance of an Egyptian named Rehman Bey. Bey announced that he had the power of suspended animation. He claimed that he could place himself in a trance. In this trance his body functions ceased. This enabled him to remain in a deathlike state for long periods of time. Doctors could not explain Bey's trances. Thousands of people were insisting that in Rehman Bey they had found proof of supernatural powers.

Bey performed his act in an airtight coffin in many New York theaters. After he entered the coffin it was covered with dirt. Bey was able to remain within the coffin for ten minutes and longer. Then Bey amazed New York by remaining in the coffin for one full hour.

There was nothing that Houdini liked better than a good challenge. He would remain longer than Bey or die in the attempt.

The coffin was lowered into the pool. Several swimmers carried it to the bottom and stood on the coffin so that it could not rise to the surface.

The coffin was equipped with a bell which Houdini could use to signal to the surface in case of emergency. It also contained a telephone. By means of the telephone, Houdini's assistant, Jim Collins, could contact the magician periodically.

The minutes ticked by slowly. A strange stillness seemed to settle over the watchers. After five minutes, Jim Collins called Houdini on the telephone. Everything was fine below.

Ten minutes passed—fifteen—twenty—twenty-five. The audience began to move restlessly. "Perhaps something is wrong," they began to murmur. Once again Collins telephoned below. Houdini's reassuring voice told him that there was no need to worry yet.

Beneath the pool Harry Houdini lay as still as possible. He knew that the slightest movement of his body would waste precious oxygen. Houdini also took long deep breaths, holding in the oxygen each time before exhaling it again.

Houdini knew that if he didn't panic and conserved his energy he could last longer than anyone thought possible. Houdini recalled the time in Detroit when he had been handcuffed and thrown into a hole in the icebound Detroit River. After freeing himself from his handcuffs, he found that he had drifted downstream. The hole was nowhere in sight.

Houdini didn't panic. He rose to the surface

and discovered an interesting fact. He learned that between the ice and the water there was a thin layer of air which made it possible for him to remain below the surface as long as he could endure the cold. Houdini took a precious breath of air. Then he began working his way upstream. Finally he located the hole in the ice and was safe.

All of these thoughts ran through Houdini's mind as he lay in the coffin. The long difficult years fighting his way to the top had been easy compared to what he was now facing.

An hour passed. Houdini had broken Rehman Bey's old record. Around the pool there was a growing concern that something had gone wrong.

The doctors looked at each other uneasily. They knew that at the age of fifty-two Houdini was not a young man. They wondered how long he could last — if he hadn't died of suffocation already.

Many around the pool were now insisting that the coffin be raised. A growing feeling of panic seemed to be sweeping the audience. Then, as if Houdini had heard the demands, the coffin suddenly shot to the surface of the pool. The swimmers had accidentally slipped off. But the coffin was immediately lowered again.

After an hour and fifteen minutes, Collins called Houdini on the telephone. Houdini reported that water was now beginning to seep into the casket. There could be no doubt that the great magician was in serious trouble. "How is he managing to breathe?" everyone asked.

Things at poolside had become serious. The crowd was in an angry mood, despite the fact that Collins reported that Houdini was still alive. Houdini had once said, "It is the element of danger that interests people. People do not wish to see me killed, of course, but they are more interested in a stunt if they think there is danger attached to it."

Houdini knew his audiences well. The element of danger was what had brought the crowd to the Shelton Hotel. But the audience was not bloodthirsty either. They wished to have no part of watching a man die before their eyes.

Finally, after an hour and a half, Houdini told Collins, "I guess I had better come up. I'm getting a little numb down here."

A group of frightened men gathered around the coffin as it was raised. Slowly the lid was pried off. From the coffin stepped the pale and haggard Houdini. He had done it. He had remained in a coffin for a full hour and a half.

The doctors examined Houdini. They were seriously alarmed at the state of his blood pressure, respiration, and body temperature. His face was a ghostly white, but his eyes still had that deep serious hypnotic stare that seemed to say, "Did you think a mere coffin could hold the Great Houdini?"

People the world over shook their heads as the news of Houdini's escape flashed around the globe. There was now no doubt in the minds of many that Harry Houdini was indeed a true spirit living on earth.

But perhaps Harry Houdini had laughed at death once too often. His time on this earth was growing short. The escape artist continued amazing audiences everywhere. But then one night in Boston the end began.

Houdini was lying on a couch in his dressing room. Three young students entered his room and asked Houdini if it was true that he could let the strongest man punch him in the stomach full force.

"Mr. Houdini, could you let me throw a punch at your midriff with all my might?" one of the young men asked. The young man happened to be a college boxer.

"Yes, certainly," replied Houdini.

"Could I try it right now?" asked the young man.

"Sure," answered Houdini confidently.

Houdini started to get up from his couch. Suddenly the young man, with everything he had, let fly with a punch to the midsection.

Houdini gasped. He hadn't been ready for the punch. The blow had severely injured the great magician.

For awhile Houdini ignored the injury. "The show must go on," he would roar when anyone tried to talk him into going to the doctor.

But the end was drawing near. The punch had caused an infection. Finally Houdini was taken to the hospital. The doctors told him that his case was hopeless.

On his last day, Bessie came in for her daily

visit. Houdini whispered in her ear, "If anything happens you must be prepared. Remember the message: 'Rosabelle, believe.' When you hear those words, know it is Houdini speaking."

It was a strange message but Bessie understood. Houdini was telling her that when he died he would try to contact her from the dead. If Bessie ever heard the words, "Rosabelle, believe," she would know that it was the Great Houdini speaking to her.

Houdini died on October 31, 1927. Strangely enough it was Halloween. Stranger even still Houdini's body was carried back to New York to be buried in the same zinc-lined coffin from which he had escaped death at the bottom of the pool of the Shelton Hotel. He would not escape this time — or would he?

THE STRANGE CASE OF
THE *MARY CELESTE*

A ship manned by skeletons? An ice-covered vessel that seeks out victims in the frozen Arctic Ocean? Since the dawn of civilization man has sought to conquer the mysteries of the sea, but returns with stories like these that stagger his imagination. Of all the unbelievable tales in the lore of the sea none can match the strange case of the *Mary Celeste*. Today debate continues on the unbelievable finding of the *Mary Celeste* on the high seas.

There is something man fears about the sea. The fury of the waves pounding against a rocky coast has been a warning to man ever since the beginning of time. It is almost as if the sea is challenging man, challenging him to try to solve the strangeness of this deep and unknown world.

From the beginning of time man has gone to sea. And from the beginning of time man has come back with strange stories that have excited him. But none of the stories matches those of the fearful tales of deserted ghost ships. These deserted ships seem to float on the sea as if steered by strange beings.

One such ship was found off the coast of South America. After coming close, a sailing boat found that the ship was covered with the green mold of the sea. The captain of the sailing ship and some of his men wanted to go on board the strange ship. The captain came near the ship in a lifeboat. He was surprised to see, through the green mold, the name of the ship. It was the *Marlborough* of Scotland. The captain couldn't believe his eyes. The *Marlborough* had been lost over 25 years ago.

Carefully, the captain went on board. He was very much afraid. At the wheel of the ship, a skeleton, still clothed, seemed to be still steering the *Marlborough*. The captain looked around and saw fully clothed skeletons everywhere on the ship. Each skeleton seemed to be at its proper place, awaiting the orders of its captain at the wheel.

Sailors in the North tell of a ship covered in ice that sails the oceans of the North, seeking out ships. The sailors of the ship *George Henry* tell with fear about the night that the ship *Rescue* seemed to attack them.

The *George Henry* was cutting its way through the icy waters off the coast of Northern Canada. Suddenly, right in front of the *George Henry*, the crew saw a ship which seemed to rise out of the sea, heading straight for them. The ship was outlined against the moon. From its masts huge pieces of ice hung like giant knives. There was no sign of life, but somehow the vessel seemed to be steering itself. Straight for the *George Henry* it came. The strange ship was now only 200 yards away! The men of the *George Henry* were in a state of fear. Now they knew that the ship coming straight for them was the long-lost ship, the *Rescue*. This ship had disappeared years before when carrying an American on a trip to the North.

The *Rescue* came closer and closer. The twisted form of the ship outlined against the moon seemed to be steered by something strange that wished only to destroy the *George Henry*.

But then, just as suddenly as the ship had appeared, it disappeared. As the men stared, the *Rescue* seemed to disappear in the fog.

But for sheer mystery, nothing can match the strange case of the *Mary Celeste*. Just to hear the name *Mary Celeste* causes sailors to shudder. The story of the *Mary Celeste*, a true story, is a strange one. It is a story without an ending, but a story that almost 100 years after it happened still is fascinating.

Captain David Morehouse of the American three-masted sailing ship *Dei Gratia* looked carefully through his long eye-piece. A little more than three miles off he could see the shape of another sailing vessel. Something about the ship interested Captain Morehouse. Try as he could, the captain could see no one aboard the vessel. Captain Morehouse could see no one at the wheel, but to his surprise the vessel seemed to be going on her course as if steered by an invisible crew.

Captain Morehouse took note of the time. It was 10 o'clock on the morning of December 4, 1872. His vessel, bound from New York to Gibraltar, was about 380 miles from the coast of Portugal. He was midway between the Azore Islands and the Portuguese coast. The sea was calm. A light wind blew from the north.

Captain Morehouse wanted to learn about this strange vessel. The *Dei Gratia* gained slowly on the vessel. Soon the distance between the two was one half-mile.

From this point Captain Morehouse could see the vessel more closely. The sailing ship was about 100 feet long, with square sails on the foremast and fore and aft sails on the mainmast.

By now the crew of the *Dei Gratia* had noted the strange ship, which was sailing in a zigzag way. The men of the *Dei Gratia* looked at each other in surprise. The bare decks of the ship and the wheel moving back and forth sent chills through them.

The *Dei Gratia* drew closer to the vessel. Captain Morehouse stared in amazement. On the front of the ship he could see the name of the vessel. It was the *Mary Celeste*. Captain Morehouse knew that the *Mary Celeste* had sailed from New York eight days before the *Dei Gratia*. In fact, Captain Morehouse and Captain Benjamin Briggs of the *Mary Celeste* were old friends. They had dined together in New York just a few days before the *Mary Celeste* left port.

Captain Morehouse knew Briggs as a good seaman. He had been a sea captain for many years with not a single bad mark on his record. Morehouse knew that Briggs was sailing with his wife Sarah, his little two-year-old daughter, and a crew of seven men. The *Mary Celeste* was carrying 1,700 barrels of alcohol from New York to Genoa, Italy. The alcohol would be used in making Italian wine.

"Do you need help?" shouted Captain Morehouse as the *Dei Gratia* drew closer to the *Mary Celeste*. His voice seemed to echo against the bow of the *Mary Celeste* and back again to the men standing on the deck of the *Dei Gratia*. The creaking of the wooden hull of the ship and the flapping of her sails were all that could be heard.

Captain Morehouse asked for a boat to be lowered and a search to begin. First Mate Oliver Deveau, Second Mate John Wright, and a sailor were ordered to board the vessel.

With some fear the party climbed aboard the ship. Deveau's eyes made a sweeping check of the deck. There wasn't a sign of life. The wheel was not locked and moved slowly back and forth. Deveau looked at Wright. Never before had the two seamen felt as they did looking at the wheel turning slowly back and forth. Deveau now called for Captain Morehouse to join them. Together they kept searching.

Signs of life were everywhere. Some shirts which had been washed only a short time before hung on a line drying. The men noticed that the ship's lifeboat was missing. Several of the sails were ripped and others were in poor shape. There was one small thing that the men wondered about. A hatch was out of place and lay wrong side up on the deck. It was close to the hatchway it had covered. But the ship, the *Mary Celeste,* was in fairly good order.

The men opened the door of the main cabin. They saw an organ. A sheet of music was still open. The cover of the organ was up as if it had just been used. On the table was a sewing machine which had just been used. On the same table was the beginning of a letter. The letter read, "Fanny, my dear wife." This was all. It was as if the writer of the letter had been stopped just as he was beginning to write.

Across the cabin Captain Morehouse saw the strangest thing that he had seen yet. A half-eaten breakfast, a plate with a little porridge on it, and an egg with the top sliced off, gave proof that someone had left the cabin in quite a hurry.

In the captain's cabin more clues were found. A gold locket and other trinkets had been left behind. The beds had all been made up, but one

51

small item gave Captain Morehouse a feeling of fear. Clearly seen on one of the pillows was the imprint of a head.

Captain Morehouse was sure that the imprint was that of Captain Briggs' young child. There was no doubt that the child had been sleeping there just a short time ago.

The ship's log had been left behind. The last entry was that of November 24, 1872. This was eleven days earlier. The entry placed the vessel near the island of Santa Maria in the Azore Islands. Somehow the *Mary Celeste* had stayed on course for eleven days. The mystery deepened. The search was kept up. Captain Morehouse found spots of blood on the deck next to the displaced hatch covers. More stains were found on the starboard rail. Close to these stains he found a deep cut which might have been made by a sharp axe.

The footsteps of the men now seemed to grow louder. The men were now sure that there was no one aboard.

"Why would a ship in good shape be left on the high seas?" thought Morehouse. But try as he could, Captain David Morehouse could not find an answer. The creaking of the hull, the soft flapping of the sails, the footsteps of the men, and the turning of the wheel back and forth, back and forth, seemed to be telling the Captain that he would never find an answer.

When Captain David Morehouse stared through his long eye-piece that day in 1872, he could not have known that his finding of the *Mary Celeste* would cause such surprise among seamen. Even today, 100 years later, men try to tell why a ship would be found left at sea with food still on the table.

The stories grew and grew until fact became mixed with fiction. Some said that a giant octopus carried the crew away.

Another story tells that a waterspout, which is a tornado at sea, lifted everyone from the deck of the ship and carried them away.

Many others note that the ship's lifeboat was missing. Maybe the crew for some unknown reason thought that the ship was going to sink or crash. Captain Briggs then told everyone to get into the lifeboat. However, the *Mary Celeste* never did crash and went on its journey, and there were no supplies taken from the *Mary Celeste*. Why would seamen get on a lifeboat without enough supplies? Also no trace was ever found of a missing lifeboat or any member of the crew of the *Mary Celeste*.

Others say that Captain Briggs killed the crew and his wife and child in a fit of anger. Then he killed himself. The blood spots seemed for awhile to back up this idea. However, it was discovered that the "blood" on a sword which was found was only rust.

Many believe that the answer to the mystery was to be found in the cargo. Perhaps gas from the alcohol formed below deck. The pressure built up until the hatch covers were blown off carrying everyone into the sea. There was little proof of an explosion to back up this story, however.

Captain Morehouse has even been called a pirate. Some thought that Captain Morehouse boarded the vessel and killed everyone aboard the *Mary Celeste*. Then he brought the ship to port for the salvage money. Actually Captain Morehouse was given almost $8,000 after he brought the *Mary Celeste* to Gibraltar. However, the captain's record had always been spotless. There was no reason to believe that he would do such a thing. In addition, the crew of the *Dei Gratia* swore to the fact that the story of the finding of the *Mary Celeste* was as Captain Morehouse had told it.

Then there are those who know the ways of the sea and the mysteries of this deep unknown world. They will tell you many stories of ships like the *Marlborough* of Scotland, found with skeletons at the wheel. They will tell of ships like the *Rescue*, the mystery ship of the North. They can tell hundreds of such stories to prove that there is an unknown force that controls the life of anyone who tries to learn the secrets of the sea. They will tell you that in 1872 the *Mary Celeste* had met the same fate as the *Rescue* and the *Marlborough* — a fate that no one will ever be able to explain.

THE LOCH NESS MONSTER —
FACT OR FICTION?

Is there a monster living in Loch Ness, in northern Scotland? Most readers scoff at the newspaper reports that tell of yet another sighting of the monster in Scotland's largest lake. Photographic evidence of the monster is ridiculed as being nothing but pictures of giant tree stumps or just plain hoaxes. Those who have searched for the monster have been viewed as slightly insane by most of the world. Yet how are we to explain the strange things that have occurred at Loch Ness over the years?

Northern Scotland is a land of rugged beauty. Mountain ranges covered with scattered trees, evergreen shrubs, and purple heather give the region a beauty that is known throughout the world. Beautiful lakes, or lochs as they are called by the Highland people, are interspersed among the rugged mountains, adding to the spectacular scenery of the entire area.

But despite the beauty there is a strange, lonely atmosphere to the Scottish Highlands. Abandoned farmhouses that once belonged to prosperous tenants dot the area. Crumbling medieval castles stand bleak and desolate in silent tribute to a romantic past. Often the mountains are covered with a cold mist. In the early morning a dense fog sometimes blankets the area, seeming to settle on the many beautiful lakes.

In the midst of the Highlands lies Loch (Lake) Ness, the largest and deepest lake in Great Britain. In recent years Loch Ness has become the center of a raging controversy. Continuing reports have been coming from Loch Ness that tell of a large animal that supposedly lives in the loch. The reports describe an animal with a small head, long neck, and enormous body. Countless sightings from reliable eyewitnesses have been reported. Disbelievers scoff at the mention of a monster living in the loch. But the evidence can no longer be ignored. An examination of some of the strange events that have occurred at Loch Ness will make even the most stubborn doubter question.

In 1952, at Loch Ness, John Cobb, the famous English speedboat enthusiast, stepped into his jet-propelled boat, the *Crusader*, to attempt bettering the world speedboat record. The waters of the loch were perfectly calm, and there was absolutely no wind blowing as the *Crusader* raced across the waters of Loch Ness. The *Crusader* reached the incredible speed of 207 miles per hour when suddenly in front of the speedboat loomed a path of large ripples. The boat struck one of the ripples with tremendous force. The impact turned the *Crusader* sideways causing it to strike the next wave. Suddenly the stillness of Loch Ness was shattered by a tremendous explosion as the *Crusader* blew apart scattering parts everywhere. John Cobb was dead.

What had caused the death of John Cobb? How could waves suddenly appear on a calm, cloudless day? Inhabitants of the area shook their heads. They knew that John Cobb's death had been caused by the Loch Ness monster. For some reason the monster, perhaps disturbed by the speedboat, had approached the surface of the loch, causing the waves and the subsequent death of John Cobb.

There never has been any explanation for John Cobb's tragic death or for the waves which suddenly appeared on the surface of Loch Ness. Indeed there has been little scientific explanation until recently for the countless mysterious sightings of whatever lives in Loch Ness.

The legend of the Loch Ness monster goes back to very early times. St. Columba, an Irish missionary who was sent to Scotland to spread Christianity, mentions sighting the monster in his writings as early as 565 A.D. Throughout the centuries since then local residents have known of the existence of the monster and can attest to sighting the creature.

But it wasn't until 1934 that a remarkable photograph, taken by a London surgeon, thrust the Loch Ness monster from the realm of superstition into the area of scientific possibility. The photograph clearly showed the neck and head of a large aquatic creature, emerging from the waters of the loch.

Dr. Wilson's photograph was greeted with mixed reactions. Some hailed it as proof that the Loch Ness monster was a reality. Others cried fraud, indicating that the photograph was either a trick or a tree stump which bore a remarkable resemblance to a living creature.

Since 1934, sightings of the monster have been reported more frequently in the newspapers. Several other photographs have appeared which are said to be of the monster. Expeditions were organized which attempted to prove or disprove the existence of the monster. None of them was able to produce any tangible evidence as to the existence of the creature.

In 1963, however, two British naturalists, Richard Fitter and Peter Scott, conceived the idea that Loch Ness should be investigated scientifically. Both men realized that a thorough investigation was the only answer.

The two men, lacking funds for their investigation, approached the British Parliament in

London. Eventually the men took their idea to David James, a Member of Parliament. At first Mr. James roared with laughter when Fitter and Scott informed him of their mission. Gradually, though, the two men convinced James that they were serious. They produced written accounts and photographs of actual sightings made of the monster. James became convinced when he examined the accounts made by reliable people.

Mr. James finally decided to visit Loch Ness himself. He interviewed fishermen, farmers, policemen, and countless other local inhabitants, many of whom claimed to have seen the monster. There was no doubt in Mr. James' mind now. Together with Richard Fitter, Peter Scott, and others, Mr. James helped found the Loch Ness Phenomena Investigation Bureau in 1963.

Twenty-four volunteers, led by Mr. James, then traveled to Loch Ness with mixed feelings about the eventual outcome of their mission. They faced a disbelieving public and even their own faith in ever achieving success was not very strong.

However, soon after arriving at Loch Ness, seven members of the expedition noticed a disturbance in the waters of the loch in Urquhart Bay, one of the deepest sections of the loch and a frequent location of monster sightings. The disturbance was caused by the splashing of a large number of salmon which were apparently trying to elude some underwater object. Then before the eyes of the seven witnesses the object began to emerge from the water. Clearly visible, the men could see two distinct humps, three feet high and 10 to 12 feet long. Luckily they were carrying their cameras and recorded the sighting with several clear photographs.

This was all that the members of the Investigation Bureau needed to convince themselves of the importance of their mission. Before long there were 80 volunteers at the loch. Donations were received from several sources and soon the Bureau was busy manning seven observation stations at various strategic locations around the loch. Each station was fully equipped with powerful cameras mounted with telephoto lenses which covered 90 percent of the loch's surface.

For some men like David James and Clem Skelton the search for the monster has now become a way of life. Skelton, resident technician of the Loch Ness Phenomena Investigation Bureau, claims to have seen the monster more times than any other person. Nothing will satisfy him until proof of the monster's existence is obtained.

Shortly after arriving at Loch Ness, Skelton was ferrying some people across the loch. The loch was clear and calm, but somehow Skelton's outboard motor gave out. There was nothing for him to do but row.

Skelton's rowing was suddenly interrupted by a noise behind him. Later he said that the noise sounded like a panting horse. Skelton stopped rowing and wheeled about. What he saw made him freeze in terror. Clearly visible, with its head and neck emerging from the water, was the monster. There could be no doubt in Clem Skelton's mind.

What Skelton said matched the description of others who have sighted the monster. The creature had a small head and a long, slim neck which gradually thickened as it reached the water. Skelton could see little of the monster's body but judging by the length and thickness of the neck he estimated that it must have been at least 40 feet long.

For several minutes Skelton stopped rowing and sat spellbound, as the monster just seemed to sit there staring at him. Then Skelton's instinct for survival overcame his fear and he began to row frantically away from the creature.

What had Clem Skelton encountered in the middle of Loch Ness? Are we to disregard the reports of eyewitnesses such as Skelton and others? Are we to pass off the sightings as examples of mass hallucination? Many reliable scientists are now convinced of the existence of a large creature or more likely a group of creatures that live in the deepest waters of Loch Ness. In fact reports have also been received from Canada, Alaska, and Russia of monsters inhabiting the deepest lakes in these areas. Although definite proof is still not available, scientists have examined every possible theory and can come to no other conclusion.

Scientists point first of all to the tremendous depth of Loch Ness. At its deepest point the loch is 754 feet deep, which makes it much deeper than the ocean waters of the nearby North Sea and English Channel. A lake of this type would be deep enough to sustain such a creature or a large school of such creatures.

The tremendous depth of Loch Ness was probably formed at the close of the ice age when the polar ice cap retreated from northern Scotland. At this time Loch Ness was probably connected to the sea. An earthquake or the retreating ice caused a shifting of the earth's surface, forming the tremendously deep lake and trapping large aquatic animals in the loch. The Loch Ness monster then is possibly a survivor of this prehistoric shifting in the earth's surface.

Loch Ness is well protected from cold winds and storms by the large mountain ranges which rise on all sides. Such protection as this would make it possible for an animal to survive from prehistoric times. In fact, the Loch is so well protected that its surface has never been known to freeze, even in the coldest weather.

Scientists also point out that the loch is separated from the sea. As a result no predatory animals such as sharks would be able to prey on creatures living in the loch.

Loch Ness is teeming with fish, including trout and salmon weighing as much as 30 pounds. The loch also contains eels as long as 10 feet.

The loch is fed by countless smaller lakes and streams which also supply a constant new source of fish. With such a large quantity of fish, survival would be possible for a creature even as large as the Loch Ness monster.

Doubters who scoff at the existence of the monster should also be made aware that several animals once thought extinct have been rediscovered in recent years. The coelacanth, a large fish thought to be extinct, was discovered in 1939 off the coast of Africa. The Komoda Dragon, the largest living lizard, also thought to be extinct, was recently discovered still living on some small islands in Indonesia. Other animals completely unknown to man have been discovered in this century as explorers penetrate into the last remaining wilderness areas and go deeper and deeper into the unknown depths of the sea.

Advanced scientific investigation seems to be the only answer to the mystery. In 1968 a research team from Birmingham University, using the newest in sonar equipment, definitely detected a large object moving along the bottom of the loch. The sonar screen showed the creature to be over 65 feet long and moving at the speed of 450 feet per minute.

Examining all of the evidence then, there is little doubt that a creature or creatures of tremendous size and speed exists in Loch Ness. Soon men such as Clem Skelton, David James, and the other members of the Loch Ness Phenomena

Investigation Bureau should have definite proof that the fabulous Loch Ness monster is more than just a fascinating legend. As a well-known scientist said recently, "There's something in Loch Ness. What it is we can't be exactly sure at this time. But there's no doubt that an animal of immense size inhabits the loch, and one of these days we're going to find it."

LINCOLN'S DREAMS

incoln had a great interest in the supernatural. He attended seances on many occasions. His own prophetic dreams foretold of coming events quite frequently. The story of our 16th president's amazing dreams will make you wonder.

Abraham Lincoln seemed to be guided by a certain sixth sense. It was almost as if he were sent by God at a time of terrible national crisis. Throughout his life Lincoln often dreamed of future events. Many times these events happened exactly as he had dreamed them.

Even as a boy, young Abe dreamed that someday he would become President of the United

States. After he became President he once said, "I had my ambitions — yes — as every American boy worth his salt has. And I dared to dream this vision of the White House — I, the humblest of the humble, born in a lowly pioneer cabin in the woods of Kentucky."

As he grew older his dreams became more frequent. On election night of 1860, Abraham Lincoln was the new President of the United States. Completely exhausted by the day's events, he lay down to rest on a sofa in his room. Suddenly in the mirror opposite where he lay, Lincoln saw two pictures of himself. In one picture he was the picture of good health. But in the other picture he was ghostly pale.

"I got up and the thing melted away," said Lincoln. "In the excitement of the hour I forgot all about it, nearly."

Several days later Lincoln was again resting on his sofa. Once again he saw the two faces. One was as pale as death and the other was the picture of good health.

This time Lincoln felt that he knew the meaning of the two faces. The face that showed good health meant that he would be successful in his first four years in office. The other face meant that he would be assassinated in his second term. As events turned out, Lincoln was killed near the end of his second term in office.

Later Lincoln met with Harriet Beecher Stowe, the woman who wrote *Uncle Tom's Cabin*, the book which exposed the evils of slavery. Lincoln told her, "Whichever way the war ends, I have the impression that I shall not last long after it is over." Lincoln died five days after the surrender of the Southern army.

As his years passed in office, Lincoln's prophetic dreams became well known by his associates. Often his dreams told him of important future events. Just before he died Lincoln called an important meeting of his cabinet. All present were waiting for news from General Sherman. Sherman was then fighting with the last of the southern armies. Lincoln told the group that he had no news as yet to report; however, he had had a dream the previous night that foretold of some great event.

Lincoln went on to relate his dream. He told of being in some kind of vessel. He was moving with great speed toward the shore. The dream was not exactly clear to Lincoln, but amazingly he had had the same dream before the battles of Sumter, Bull Run, Antietam, Gettysburg, Stone River, and Wilmington.

Lincoln said that the dream usually preceded good news. "I think it must be from Sherman. My thoughts are in that direction," he said.

But the most famous of all of Lincoln's dreams came only one month before his assassination. The President kept silent about it for some time, but at last he could not help but mention it to a few friends.

One night the President was entertaining friends in the Red Room. At ten o'clock tea and cakes were served and shortly afterward most of the guests began to leave.

The war was over but Mr. Lincoln's face looked long and solemn. The President said that his mind was heavy. Expectantly, the gathering of friends looked toward him.

The President began to talk about dreams. He sat forward with his elbows on his knees.

"Nowadays dreams are regarded as very foolish, and as seldom told except by old women and by young men and maidens in love," he said.

Mrs. Lincoln looked worried. "Why?" she said. "Do you believe in dreams?"

"I can't say that I do," Lincoln replied. "But I had one the other night which has haunted me ever since."

"You frighten me!" cried Mrs. Lincoln. "What is the matter?"

"I am afraid that I have done wrong to mention the subject at all. But somehow the thing has gotten possession of me."

Mr. Lincoln tried to talk of other things, but Mrs. Lincoln kept returning to the dream. Finally Mr. Lincoln agreed to tell the story.

"About three days ago I retired very late. I had been up waiting for important dispatches from the front. I could not have been long in bed when I fell into a slumber, for I was weary. I soon began to dream. There seemed to be a deathlike stillness about me.

"Then I heard subdued sobs, as if a number of people were weeping. I thought I left my bed

68

and wandered downstairs. There the silence was broken by the same pitiful sobbing, but the mourners were invisible. I went from room to room, but no living person was in sight — yet the same mournful sounds of distress met me as I passed along. It was light in all the rooms. Every object was familiar to me. But where were all the people who were grieving as if their hearts would break? I was puzzled and alarmed. What could be the meaning of all this?

"Determined to find the cause of a state of things so mysterious and so shocking, I kept on until I arrived at the East Room, which I entered. There I met with a sickening surprise. Before me was a catafalque, on which rested a corpse wrapped in funeral vestments. Around it were stationed soldiers who were acting as guards. And there was a throng of people, some gazing mournfully upon the corpse, whose face was covered, others weeping pitifully."

" 'Who is dead in the White House?' I demanded of one of the soldiers. 'The President,' was his answer; 'he was killed by an assassin!' Then came a loud burst of grief from the crowd, which woke me from my dream. I slept no more that night. And although it was only a dream, I have been strangely annoyed by it ever since."

"That is horrid!" Mrs. Lincoln said. "I wish you had not told me it. I am glad I don't believe in dreams, or I should be in terror from this time forth."

"Well," replied the President, "it is only a

69

dream, Mary. Let us say no more about it, and try to forget it."

As the time of his death drew closer and closer, Lincoln seemed to sense more and more that the end was drawing near. On the afternoon before he died, President Lincoln was talking with his trusted guard, William Crook.

"Crook, do you know, I believe there are men who want to take my life and I have no doubt they will do it."

"Why do you think so, Mr. President?" Crook asked.

"Other men have been assassinated," Lincoln replied.

"I hope you are mistaken, Mr. President," Crook replied, refusing to believe Lincoln's words.

"I have perfect confidence in those around me, in every one of you men," said Lincoln slowly. "I know no one could do it and escape alive. But if it is to be done, it is impossible to prevent it."

That evening Crook was going off duty. He turned to the President and said good night to him. Lincoln replied, "Good-bye, Crook."

On his way home Crook thought over the President's last words. Mr. Lincoln had always said "Good night, Crook," but never "Good-bye."

Three hours after President Lincoln said good-bye to his guard William Crook he was shot while attending a play at the Ford Theatre in Washington, D.C.

The nation and the world were shocked. President Lincoln was gone. But perhaps in some mysterious way his presence is still helping to guide our great nation. There are those who are sure that he still watches over our nation's leaders just as he did a century ago. It would be comforting to think that this is true.

THE LOST PATROL

Is it possible for an airplane to be lost without leaving a single trace or clue? Can a plane in constant radio contact, fully equipped with the most modern equipment, simply disappear? Off the southern coast of the United States there is an area called the Bermuda Triangle. In this area over a hundred planes and ships have been lost. No trace has ever been found of any of them. The story of "The Lost Patrol" is the most famous of all the stories from the mysterious area of the Bermuda Triangle. It is a story that you won't believe, but it is completely true.

On the night of June 5, 1965, Louis Guintoli and 10 men climbed into a twin-engine C-119 Flying

Boxcar at Holmestead Air Force Base in Florida. The plane was headed for Grand Turk Island in the Bahama Islands. It was a routine flight, and the weather was perfect as the plane soared into the air.

About 100 miles from Grand Turk Island, Guintoli reported that all was well. Then, shortly afterward, radio operators in Florida began to lose contact with the Boxcar. Soon all radio contact was lost. The plane was never heard from again.

The following day and for days afterward planes and ships searched the entire area. No trace of the plane or its men was ever found.

On the night of January 29, 1948, the *Star Tiger* with 29 people on board was flying, in perfectly calm weather, approximately 400 miles northeast of Bermuda. The captain of the four-engined British plane routinely reported to the control tower that his engines were running smoothly and that he expected to land in Bermuda on time. The captain's final words were, "Arriving on schedule."

The *Star Tiger* and its passengers and crew were never heard from again. Planes and ships searched the area, but once again not a single trace was ever found. The *Star Tiger* had disappeared.

Almost a year later the *Star Ariel*, sister ship of the *Star Tiger*, took off from Bermuda carrying 20 passengers and crew. There was hardly a cloud in the sky as the plane departed.

About 25 minutes after take off, the pilot radioed back the familiar words, "All's well." Then his voice faded. This was the last that anyone heard from the *Star Ariel*. Like the *Star Tiger*, no clues were ever found. Oddly enough the two planes were lost within 600 miles of each other.

On August 28, 1963, two four-engine jets were flying on a mission three hundred miles southwest of Bermuda. Once again the two planes were in radio contact with land; again the voices faded. No trace of the jets was ever found.

Each year more and more ships and planes have been disappearing off the southwest coast of the United States, in an area that has become known as the Bermuda Triangle. The area covers a large portion of ocean roughly forming a huge triangle. The perimeter of the triangle extends from Bermuda to the coast of Florida to the island of Puerto Rico.

As the years pass the mystery grows deeper. At first, experts laughed off the puzzle of the Bermuda Triangle, claiming that it was only a matter of bad luck that so many planes had been lost in this small part of the world. But with each disappearance, with each lost ship or plane, even the experts have been forced to admit that there is something strange going on in the area of the Bermuda Triangle.

Over 100 planes and ships have been swallowed up by this watery grave. Each disappearance is a story all of its own. But none of the tales of missing airplanes can match that of the story of The Lost Patrol. The finding of the *Mary Celeste* has become the most talked about sea story ever told. Perhaps more frightening, more mysterious is the story of The Lost Patrol.

It was 2:10 P.M. on the afternoon of December 5, 1945, when five Avenger torpedo bombers coasted onto the runway at the Fort Lauderdale, Florida, Naval Air Station.

Lt. Charles Taylor, the flight leader, looked over the Avengers. They had just been checked carefully and were in perfect running order. The gas tanks were full; the engines and controls were working smoothly. Each plane had a large life raft big enough for several men, and each crew member carried a life jacket.

Five officers and nine crew members had been assigned to the five Avengers. Their job was a simple one. They were to fly 160 miles east over the Atlantic Ocean. Then they were to turn north for forty miles and then head back for Fort Lauderdale.

It was a routine flight. The pilots and crews had made hundreds of such flights. With each one of the men well-trained in his job, little could go wrong on such a flight.

The Avengers streaked down the runway and rose into the sky. Flying conditions were ideal as the planes headed toward the blue Atlantic.

The Avengers had been in the air a little over an hour when Naval Air Station radiomen picked up a strange, garbled message from Lt. Taylor.

They couldn't understand Lt. Taylor's words but one thing was certain. Lt. Taylor and the rest of the flight were in trouble.

A few minutes later the radiomen picked up another strange message. Lt. Taylor was trying to talk to another pilot in the patrol. "Can't see land . . . can't be sure where we are . . . we are not sure of our position. . . ."

The radiomen were baffled. What could be wrong? They tried desperately to make contact with the flight, but all they could get were confused, garbled words.

Shortly after this another strange message was picked up. "Where are we? It looks like the world rolled over. . . . It's all white around me. . . ."

Then the radiomen heard a very unusual thing. It was the voice of Lt. Taylor turning over command of the flight to another pilot.

Shortly after, the new flight leader tried to reach Fort Lauderdale. "Not certain where we are. . . . Everything is wrong . . . strange. . . . We can't be sure of any direction. Even the ocean doesn't look as it should."

The voice of the pilot was now in a complete state of panic. Once again his voice cracked, "We think we must be about 225 miles northeast of the base. . . . Looks like we are . . ."

The radio went silent, completely silent.

Rescue plans were quickly initiated. A twin-engine Martin Mariner with a crew of 13 men carrying full rescue and survival equipment was sent immediately to the scene. The huge flying boat had a specially built hull which enabled it to land in the roughest seas.

Shortly after takeoff, the Naval Base began to receive reports from the Mariner describing the flying conditions and other routine information. But amid all the reports there was no mention of the missing plane.

At 6:30 P.M. Lt. H. G. Cone reported from the Mariner that wind from the west was weak at low altitude but strong above 6,000 feet. These were the last words ever heard from the Mariner.

As night approached six airplanes were missing. Five Avengers had seemingly been swallowed in a watery grave. Then unbelievably the Martin Mariner sent in search of the Avengers was missing too. Coast Guard vessels from Miami raced to the area where the planes had last reported. Naval aircraft from a dozen air stations came to the rescue.

By dawn one of the biggest searches in naval history had been launched. By eight o'clock 330 planes and 21 ships were searching frantically for the lost planes.

By midmorning the Carrier *Solomans* arrived, dispatching 30 planes which joined in the search. Planes from the British Royal Air Force and ships from the Royal Navy joined in the gigantic rescue operation.

For five days the area of the Atlantic Ocean was crossed and crisscrossed. Every single square mile of ocean was covered in one of the most thorough searches in naval history. In addition, even land parties searched thousands of miles of shoreline for possible traces of the missing aircraft.

No sign of the six planes was ever found.

Six fully equipped planes had somehow vanished. Not a single trace was ever discovered. There was no oil slick or visible wreckage. The bodies of the airmen were never recovered. Not a single piece of the six planes has been recovered to this day. The Bermuda Triangle had claimed six more victims. Twenty-seven men had somehow vanished from the face of the earth.

How could it have happened? Each plane carried powerful radios. Yet no warning, no SOS, was ever received. Each man carried a parachute which was to be used in an emergency. Each plane was equipped with life rafts and flares, also for emergency use. All 27 men on the plane had been well-trained in survival techniques.

Could the planes have exploded in midair? This idea was ruled out. An explosion would leave remains which would have been seen.

Every possible cause for the disaster was checked and rechecked. At the end of the investigation the Navy gave its answer, "We were not able to make even a good guess as to what happened."

Many theories were advanced in the disappearance of The Lost Patrol. Some experts say that the Bermuda Triangle is one of the chief centers for the sighting of flying saucers in the world. Perhaps ships and planes are flying into a huge trap in which UFOs are waiting in hiding.

Others say that the area is one of the most unusual in the world as far as weather conditions are concerned. It is the area in which many of the largest hurricanes begin. Perhaps in some unexplainable way the planes were lost by some freak occurrence in the weather, which is still unknown to man.

Thus the mystery of the Bermuda Triangle remains a secret to this day. Only the men of the missing planes like the five Avengers and the Martin Mariner could really tell us what happened. But they are part of The Lost Patrol.

THE INVASION OF
THE MARTIANS

The literature of science fiction contains countless stories of attacks from outer space. The stories tell how Earth is invaded by fantastic creatures from another world. The inhabitants of Earth are then thrown into a state of panic in an effort to repel the invaders. Yet no science-fiction story can ever match the true story of what happened on Halloween evening of 1938, the day that Martians "invaded" Earth. The events of this evening are so strange that even today we find them difficult to believe. Yet they happened! The following recreation of that memorable evening will match and even surpass the events of any science-fiction story that you will ever read because everything that happened in the following pages is absolutely true.

On the evening of October 31, 1938, strange things began happening all over the United States. In St. Louis hundreds of people stood on street corners looking to the sky, their faces twisted with fear. In Newark 20 screaming families burst from an apartment building holding wet towels and handkerchiefs over their faces. They screamed that they were being attacked by gas. In Pittsburgh a man returning home from work found his wife holding a bottle of poison and screaming, "I'd rather go like this than like that!"

What was the cause of these and hundreds of other strange events that happened all over the country on this night? Unbelievably, the events were caused by a radio play. It was a play so real, so well-performed, that those who heard it were certain that the end of the world had come. Now, more than 30 years later, the events of this fantastic evening sound hard to believe. But they did happen.

This now-famous Halloween evening started just as any other pre-World War II Sunday evening. Americans of the time kept their ears glued to the radio, listening for news from Europe. Hitler's armies had already entered Austria and were ready to march into Poland. In the Far East there was more and more talk of Japan's growing power. It was an uneasy time for the world.

Perhaps this had something to do with the unbelievable events of this Halloween evening.

Millions of Americans just tuning in their radios shortly after eight o'clock heard a "news commentator" report that strange things were happening on the planet Mars. The commentator spoke slowly, measuring each word:

We know now that in the early years of the 20th century this world was being watched closely by beings more intelligent than man. We know that as man went about his daily work he was being watched closely and studied. Minds far greater than his own watched the earth and drew their plans against us.

The announcer continued talking. The radio listener who had just turned on his radio was bound to be captured by the man's way of speaking. Then the voice was interrupted by another announcer:

We take you to the Meridian Room in the Hotel Park Plaza in downtown New York. You will be listening soon to the music of Ramon Raquello and his orchestra.

Soft dance music came from the radio. Then another announcer in a more excited voice spoke. He reported that several gas explosions had been reported on the planet Mars. The gas seemed to be moving toward Earth with tremendous velocity. The announcer described the gas as being like a jet of blue flame. Then, as his voice faded, the dance music of "Ramon Raquello" played the well-known song "Stardust."

By this time millions of listeners everywhere had moved closer to their radios so as not to miss a word. Those who had tuned in at eight o'clock knew that it was just a play. They knew that it was a broadcast presented by the Mercury Theater, based on H. G. Wells' famous book, *The War of the Worlds*. For most of these listeners there was no problem. It was just an interesting radio drama. But for those who tuned in after the program had started, it was a different story. They were used to hearing sudden news reports of destruction from Europe and Asia. This broadcast sounded real. The announcer's voice was too grave.

The program continued. The announcer, his voice growing louder, less sure, spoke:

Ladies and gentlemen, here is a special report from Trenton, New Jersey. At 8:50 P.M. a huge glowing object, believed to be a meteorite, fell to Earth. It landed on a farm near Grovers Mill, New Jersey, 22 miles from Trenton.

We have sent a special unit to the spot. Soon you will hear the voice of our commentator, Mr. Carl Phillips.

Dance music once again came from the radio. Then the voice of "Carl Phillips" could be heard speaking.

In front of me I can see the — the thing. It is half buried in a huge pit . . . . From what I can see, the object itself doesn't look very much like a meteor. It is about 30 yards wide. It has a yellow-white color.

Spectators are moving close to the object. Police are trying to keep the crowd back, but they aren't having much luck.

Phillips next spoke with a "Mr. Wilmuth," owner of the farm. Mr. Wilmuth said that he had been listening to the radio. Suddenly he was knocked right out of his chair.

Phillips now spoke to a "Professor Pierson" from Princeton University. Professor Pierson seemed to doubt that the thing was a meteor, but the professor seemed as confused as everyone else by the object.

Now terrified voices from the crowd could be heard. There was fear and panic in the voices. Phillips continued:

Ladies and gentlemen, this is the most terrifying thing I have ever seen. Wait a minute! Someone is crawling out of the top! Someone . . . or . . . something!

A loud cry from the crowd drowned out Phillips' voice. Then he went on speaking, almost shouting:

Good heavens, something is wriggling out of the shadows. It is like a gray snake. Now there's another one, and another. They look like huge arms to me. There, I can see the thing's body. It's as large as a bear. It is shining like wet leather. But that face. It — it's impossible to describe. I can hardly force myself to keep looking at it. The eyes are black and gleam like a snake's. The monster is rising up!

84

There was a pause that seemed like hours. Then the excited voice of Phillips could be heard again saying that the police captain and two policemen were approaching the thing, carrying a flag of truce.

A loud hissing noise could be heard. This was followed by a humming sound that grew louder and louder. Phillips continued:

A humped shape is rising out of the pit. I can make out a small beam of light against a mirror. What's that? There's a jet of flame coming from the mirror. It is coming right at the advancing men. It strikes them head on! Oh, no, they're turning into flame!

There was a loud crash as the microphone fell to the ground. Then there was silence — complete silence. Not a single word could be heard coming from the radio.

By this time in the broadcast, reports were coming in from all over the country to police stations, newspaper offices, and radio stations of the strange effect the show was having. Hardest hit of all were those places close to "Grovers Mill." Reports reached the state police in nearby Trenton that the roads in the area were jammed. Many people had packed all of their things and were trying desperately to escape. Many others, armed with all kinds of weapons, were rushing to "Grovers Mill" to see if they could help.

In Caldwell, New Jersey, a man rushed into a church saying that a meteor had fallen, killing thousands. In Jersey City, a man rushed into a police station demanding that he be given a gas mask. In Newark, a woman stumbled out of her apartment screaming, "Don't you know New Jersey is destroyed by the Germans! It's on the radio!"

As the play continued, even stranger things began to happen. The voice of a new announcer reported that the burned body of Carl Phillips had been identified in a Trenton hospital. The announcer reported that he was going to turn the broadcast over to Captain Lansing of the state militia.

There was a slight delay. Then a deep voice spoke. The voice sounded confident, extremely sure of itself, explaining that 7,000 men were closing in. Lansing, the new announcer, continued in amazement:

Wait! . . . It's something moving . . . solid metal . . . lind of shieldlike affair coming up out of the cylinder. It's going higher and higher. Why, it's standing on legs—actually standing on a sort of metal frame. Now it's reaching above the trees. The searchlights are on it! Hold on!

Then there was a long pause. The announcer spoke in a very serious voice:

Ladies and gentlemen, I have a grave announcement to make. Incredible as it may seem, these strange beings who landed in the Jersey farmlands tonight are the first part of an invading army from the planet Mars. The battle which took place tonight at Grovers

*Mill has ended. It is one of the worst defeats ever
suffered by any army. Seven thousand men armed with
rifles and machine guns have been destroyed by a
single fighting machine.*

The announcer reported that the Martian
machines were now beginning to move north.
More metal monsters had now joined the others.
They had passed the town of Somerville and
were now in the Watchung Mountains. The
enemy was now turning east and had crossed the
Passaic River into the Jersey marshes. The announcer reported that the monsters must be
headed toward New York City.

Many in New York were thrown into a state
of panic by the news. Men and women rushed
into a police station, shouting that they had
their things packed and were ready to leave. One
man was certain that he heard President Roose-
velt's voice on the radio telling everyone to leave
the city. A man ran into another police station
shouting that enemy planes were crossing the
Hudson River.

In downtown New York, a woman rushed into
a theatre screaming that the end of the world
had come.

In Queens, people called the police stations
wondering if the poison gas would reach them.

In Brooklyn, thousands stood on street corners searching the sky for signs of the "Martians."

Newspaper offices were jammed with calls.
One man called *The New York Times* from Day-

ton, Ohio. "What time will it be the end of the world?" he wanted to know.

The radio drama was now reaching its climax. By this time in the play the Martians were close to New York City. The end appeared near as an announcer spoke. His voice was now desperate:

Ladies and gentlemen, I am speaking to you from New York City. The streets are all jammed. The noise is tremendous. The enemy can now be seen above the Palisades. There are five great machines. The first one is crossing the river. I can see it from here. It is crossing the Hudson River like a man wading a small brook. I have just been handed a bulletin. Martian cylinders are falling all over the country. One outside Buffalo, one in Chicago, another in St. Louis. The first machine has reached the shore. It stands watching, looking over the city. Its steel head is as high as the skyscrapers. He waits for the others. They rise like a line of new towers on the city's west side. Now they're lifting their metal hands. This is the end now. Smoke comes out . . . black smoke, drifting over the city. People in the streets see it now. They're running toward the East River . . . thousands of them, dropping in like rats. Now the smoke is spreading faster. It's reached Times Square. People are trying to run away from it, but it's no use.

They're falling like flies. Now the smoke is crossing Fifth Avenue . . . Sixth Avenue . . . 100 yards . . . It's 50 feet . . . it . . .

Then there was silence, complete silence. The end of the world had come — at least it seemed

88

that way to millions of radio listeners. Then a radio announcer's voice could be heard.

You are listening to the broadcast of Orson Welles and the Mercury Theater on the Air. This is an original broadcast of the War of the Worlds by H. G. Wells. The broadcast will continue after a short intermission.

The spell had been broken. The show continued. The second half of the play told the tale of a lone survivor of the Martian invasion. The survivor wandered across the land. He wandered into New York City where he saw the dead bodies of the Martians. They had been killed, not by bullets or bombs, but by the only thing they couldn't fight against — germs in the Earth's atmosphere. The Martians, used to a different atmosphere, could not live for long on Earth.

No one listened very carefully to the second half of the program however. People were too angry. They knew now that the whole thing had been only a play. They were annoyed at being "tricked."

As the effects of the play became known, people centered their anger at Orson Welles. Welles was a 23-year-old, six-foot, 200-pounder. He was known as the "boy genius" of radio broadcasting. He had first become famous as the voice of *The Shadow*, one of the most popular mystery shows at the time.

Anger at Welles was nationwide. After the program was over, the mayor of a large western city called the station on the telephone. He was so angry he could barely speak. He reported mobs in the streets of his city. Women and children were huddled in churches. The mayor had just learned that the whole thing was only a play. He announced that he personally was coming to New York to punch Welles in the nose.

In defense of Welles, it was said that he had no idea that his radio broadcast would cause such a stir. It was announced at the beginning of the show and several times after that it was only a play. It was those who turned their dials to the play in the middle who were affected the most.

For days after the play, newspapers across the country began carrying reports of the play's strange effects. From Indianapolis came the story that a woman had run into a church screaming, "New York is destroyed. It's the end of the world. You might as well go home to die. I just heard it on the radio."

In Providence, the electric company received hundreds of calls. The callers demanded that all lights be turned off so that the city would be safe.

In Boston, a woman called the police. She said that she could "see the fire."

In Kansas City, a man called and said that he had loaded his wife and children in his car; he had filled it with gas and was going somewhere. "Where is it safe?" he asked.

From New England, newspapers received a report of a woman who had really become scared. "I kept shivering and shaking," the woman said. "I pulled out suitcases and put them back, started to pack but didn't know what to take. I kept piling clothes on my baby, took all her clothes out, and wrapped her up. Everybody went out of the house except the neighbor upstairs. I ran up and banged on his door. He wrapped two of his children in blankets and I carried the other, and my husband carried my child. We rushed out. I don't know why, but I wanted to take some bread, for I thought that if everything is burning you can't eat money, but you can eat bread."

But the feeling of the country could best be summed up by the words of a man from upper New York state. "I thought the whole human race was going to be wiped out — that seemed more important than the fact that we were going to die. It seemed awful that everything that had been worked on for years was going to be lost forever."

Orson Welles certainly had given the country a Halloween scare that it would never forget.

OUTER SPACE EXPERIMENT
IN ESP

ave you ever had the feeling that something was going to happen to you — and it did? Have you ever had a dream of some event that later came true? Have you ever been thinking of a person in another town only to have that person call you on the phone at precisely the moment you were thinking of him? If you have, then you may have had a simple experience in extrasensory perception.

Long ridiculed by most as mere coincidences or even as forms of witchcraft, ESP has slowly been converting its doubters into believers. Then, in February of 1971, a dramatic experiment in ESP aboard Apollo 14, the

fourth spaceship to transport men to the moon, attempted to prove scientifically the existence of the mysterious "sixth sense."

The ground at Cape Kennedy, Florida, vibrated as the huge Saturn 5 engine roared to its full power. Billowing orange smoke rushed from the huge rocket. For 8.9 seconds after ignition, *Apollo 14*'s engines roared to a full thrust of nearly 8,000,000 pounds. Then the four steel restraining arms which held the rocket in place retracted, exposing the gigantic rocket to the rays of the morning sunlight.

Slowly the rocket struggled against the Earth's gravity. It seemed for a breathtaking second that *Apollo 14* would be unable to lift itself into the atmosphere. Then slowly it began to rise. In eight seconds it had cleared the launching tower. Then it began to pick up speed as it headed into the low hanging clouds which for awhile had threatened to postpone the launching.

Apollo 14 was headed toward the moon. It was January 31, 1971, the 13th anniversary of our nation's first satellite launching. On January 31, 1958, a 70-foot unmanned *Jupiter* C rocket lifted the 30.5 *Explorer 1* capsule into orbit around the earth. It was a humble beginning but a beginning nevertheless.

Then, in 1961, a Redstone rocket, the first American manned spaceflight was launched from Cape Kennedy. Commanded by Alan Shepard, Jr., and Virgil Grissom, *Freedom 7* rocketed 116.5

miles into the sky and 302 miles down range from the launching site. It was an important if modest beginning compared with the more spectacular flights to come.

Apollo 14 marked a landmark in space exploration in many ways. For one it marked the return to space flight of Alan Shepard, one of America's first space heroes. Scheduled to fly the first two-manned mission into space in 1963, Shepard was suddenly grounded. He had somehow developed an ailment in the inner ear, causing dizziness and nausea. Eventually the disease could lead to total deafness.

Unable to stay away from the exciting world of space flight altogether, Shepard took a job as chief of the astronaut office. But it was not the real thing for Captain Shepard. Wishing to be personally involved in the Apollo voyages to the moon, Shepard went to a Los Angeles physician. The physician planted a small tube in Shepard's ear which successfully drained the fluid from the inner ear to a spinal cavity.

Now Shepard, the "old man" of space flight at the age of 47, once again found himself in the limelight. Together with fellow astronauts Stuart Roosa and Edgar Mitchell he hoped to explore the Fra Mauro region of the moon. Fra Mauro is a hilly range thought to contain a wealth of geological information which could eventually reveal facts which would even tell of the origins of the universe.

Apollo 14 also represented a pivotal flight in the

Apollo series. Apollo flights eight through 12 had been near perfect space flights. But *Apollo 13* had resulted in a near disaster.

The explosion of an oxygen tank had left *Apollo 13's* command module without power. Astronauts Fred Hause, James Lovell, and John Swigert were forced to rely on the lunar module for electricity, heat, and water on the return trip from the moon. It was a close call.

The fact that something unforeseen had actually happened in space threatened the continuation of all future manned space exploration. The spacecrafts that were once thought to be faultless now had to prove themselves all over again.

Astronauts Shepard, Mitchell, and Roosa were trained to a peak of proficiency for the *Apollo 14* voyage. A delay of three months in the project had enabled the team to spend hundreds of hours in spacecraft simulation, responding to emergencies of every kind.

The crew of *Apollo 14* was composed of three of the best qualified men in the space program. Captain Shepard, the most experienced of the astronauts, was the picture of self-confidence. Despite his 47 years, Captain Shepard had the reflexes and stamina of a man 10 years younger.

Thirty-eight-year-old Major Stuart Roosa, who would pilot the command module as Shepard and Mitchell walked on the moon, was also a veteran of the space program. Major Roosa, like the others, knew the dangers that faced the crew. Major Roosa had been the last man to speak to the three astronauts who lost their lives aboard *Apollo 1*.

Apollo 14 was fortunate in having aboard Commander Edgar Mitchell, a highly qualified astronaut with a reputation for being one of the most intelligent men in the entire space program. Commander Mitchell was endowed with an insatiable curiosity that went far beyond scientific data. Commander Mitchell was interested in the workings of the human mind, and during his free moments aboard *Apollo 14* hoped to experiment in the area of extrasensory perception.

"I think we are learning and have learned that there is a great deal about the human mind, the human spirit, the essences of humanity, that is somewhat different from what we've thought in the past," Commander Mitchell had once remarked.

As a young boy Edgar Mitchell was possessed of an enquiring mind. From his earliest days, young Edgar was fascinated by aviation and the mysteries of space. Born in Hereford, Texas, on September 17, 1930, Edgar grew up close to a small airfield. He worshiped the crop-dusting pilots who flew old biplanes from the tiny airfield. Before long young Edgar used to scrub down planes in exchange for free rides.

Edgar Mitchell's education was a highly technical one, fully equipping him for the challenge of space flight. He graduated with a Bachelor of Science degree in industrial management from Carnegie in 1952; a Bachelor of Science degree in aeronautical engineering from the U.S. Navy's Postgraduate School in 1962; and a Doctor of Science degree from Massachusetts Institute of Technology in 1964. "My academic credentials were planned with the space program in mind," said Mitchell.

As *Apollo 14* headed for the moon, the next few days promised to yield scientific data invaluable to mankind. Not only did the astronauts plan to observe many facets of the moon with complex scientific instruments, but in the person of Commander Mitchell another type of experiment was about to take place — far different from any experiment ever conducted in outer space.

For awhile Commander Mitchell's duties aboard *Apollo 14* occupied almost all of his time. There were few free moments as the rocket left its orbit around the Earth and headed for a lunar orbit. But then as the huge rocket settled on its course, Commander Mitchell began his experiment. The plan consisted of a simple experiment in thought transference, or telepathy, one of the three branches of extrasensory perception.

Commander Mitchell hoped to serve as a "sender" of thought-messages back to Earth. On Earth, four specially selected persons would serve as "receivers" in attempting to receive Commander Mitchell's thought-messages.

For his experiment Commander Mitchell planned on using the well-known Zener cards. The cards were named after Mr. K. E. Zener, an early researcher in the area of extrasensory perception. Together with Dr. J. B. Rhine of Duke University, one of the most well-known researchers in the entire field, Zener developed a set of 25 cards which he and Dr. Rhine used to conduct countless ESP experiments.

The cards are a simple but conclusive method of determining ESP ability. One person acts as a sender and the other as a receiver. The sender shuffles the cards and puts them face down on a table. He or she then picks up one of the cards and concentrates on the card, at the same time attempting to transfer his thoughts to the receiver. The receiver in turn tries to concentrate on the thought message and attempts to name the card that the sender has chosen.

Results using Zener cards will vary from individual to individual. Some receivers are highly responsive to thought messages. One of the most exciting discoveries in the history of ESP involved a man named Hubert Pearce. Working with Dr. Rhine at Duke University, it was discovered that Pearce scored remarkably high in testing Zener cards. Pearce, a young divinity student, averaged scores of five to 10 hits above chance. A hit is a correct identification of a Zener card. The odds against these high scores on a consistent basis are billions to one. A set of Zener cards contains 25 cards. The set consists of five circles, five crosses, five wavy lines, five squares, and five stars. The laws of chance would give a person five correct responses in each set of 25 guesses.

Other individuals have become known for their ESP ability. A nine-year-old girl named Amy had the remarkable ability of identifying ordinary playing cards with an amazingly high degree of accuracy; Amy was able to identify 24 cards correctly out of a deck of 52 cards. She also identified 18 others correctly but named the suit incorrectly. Remarkably enough, Amy had missed completely on only ten guesses. The odds against such a performance are millions to one.

ESP experiments were nothing new even in the world of exploration. In 1933, a group of Russian fliers crashed somewhere in the area of the North Pole. Sir Hubert Wilkins, an Arctic explorer, set out in an attempt to rescue the lost flyers. But before his departure he agreed to try to contact, across thousands of miles, Harold Sherman, a well-known mentalist, by way of mental-messages.

While Wilkins was looking for the lost flyers, he projected his thoughts to Sherman in his New York apartment. Both the sender, Wilkins, and the receiver, Sherman, kept diaries of their thoughts. Each night the two men sent records of their messages to Dr. Gardner Murphy. Remarkably enough Dr. Murphy discovered that the messages matched in over 70 percent of the entries.

On Armistice Day in 1937 Sherman clearly "saw" in his mind's eye Wilkin's' plane forced down in a blizzard. Right after this he perceived an image of the explorer waltzing at a dress ball. At the time the image made little sense to him.

Ten days later, however, when Wilkins' report arrived, the image became clear. Wilkins' plane, in an emergency flight to Saskatchewan, had been forced down during a blizzard in Regina, Canada. In Regina, Wilkins was invited to attend an Armistice Day Ball. The mystery of the strange image was cleared up. The distance between the two men was approximately 3,500 miles, lending support to the theory that distance does not affect extrasensory messages.

It was this fact that Commander Mitchell wished to prove. Mitchell like many others was quite familiar with the countless cases of spontaneous ESP experiences. For years Dr. Rhine at Duke University, and other scientists in the field of parapsychology, had been conducting planned scientific experiments in ESP. But no one had ever tried an ESP experiment across a quarter of a million miles of space.

Commander Mitchell's experiment called for the transferring of thought messages on six separate occasions through the use of Zener cards. On Earth, four specially selected receivers would attempt to record the sequence of cards sent by Mitchell.

One of the receivers on earth was Olaf Jonsson, a Chicago drafting engineer well-known for his telepathic ability. Jonsson, who had attracted considerable fame for his psychic feats, claimed to have been aware of his gift since the age of six. As time went on Jonsson amazed his friends with his uncanny ability. Once, when buying a car, Jonsson bargained with the salesman, knowing in his mind the lowest bid that the salesman would accept. The two finally agreed on the exact sales figure that Jonsson had predicted. During World War II, Jonsson helped the captain of his ship detect unknown mine fields on at least twenty occasions. When Jonsson was selected for the ESP experiment with Mitchell he was put through a series of tests. He excelled in all of them.

Because of time limitations aboard *Apollo 14*, Mitchell was only able to conduct his experiment on four occasions. On each experiment Mitchell reshuffled the deck of 25 Zener cards. He then concentrated on each card in its turn, attempting to transfer his thoughts through space back to Earth.

On earth the four receivers, working on a prearranged time schedule, also focused their thoughts in an effort to receive the messages sent by Mitchell. In Chicago, Olaf Jonsson began each session with at least a half hour of meditation and preparation for reception.

In all, Commander Mitchell was able to transfer eight runs or two hundred guesses back to his four receivers.

However, for Commander Mitchell, interest in ESP was temporarily forgotten as *Apollo 14* got closer to the moon. Exciting days of orbiting the moon and then actually walking on the moon followed as millions of amazed viewers watched on television. The results of his ESP experiments would have to wait until *Apollo 14* returned to Earth.

Apollo 14's safe return and the subsequent picking up of the three astronauts in the Pacific Ocean were hailed by a waiting nation.

Captain Alan Shepard was overjoyed. "I can intuitively tell from what we've done, what we've seen on the surface [of the moon], that we're bringing back a wealth of information photographically and geologically, and we've left a station, another station, on the moon, sending back information for scientific purposes. I think that generally speaking it was a smash success."

For Commander Mitchell the scientific success of the mission was gratifying. Analysis of the results of the ESP experiments, although optimistic, were inconclusive. In Chicago, Olaf Jonsson said, "At times I was 100 percent sure I saw the cards clearly. But other times the image was blurred."

An analysis of the 200 thought messages sent back to Earth revealed some interesting statistics, however. Two of the four receivers correctly identified 51 of the two hundred cards. Since pure chance would account for forty correct responses, 51 correct guesses seemed to indicate ESP transfer. Mitchell dismissed the results as inconclusive, however. "This is an acceptable significant result in other sciences, but parapsychology is more conservative and considers such odds as only suggestive of extrasensory performance," Mitchell said.

Analysis of the other receivers revealed a startling result. One receiver correctly identified only 35 cards. This result is so far below chance that the odds are approximately 3,000 to 1 against it. However, this was highly interesting to Mitchell, since it revealed a well-known fact of ESP research known as "negative" ESP.

Early investigators in ESP research found that some subjects scored considerably below chance in test after test. For awhile the researchers were baffled by this odd phenomenon. Now it is realized that low scoring is just as indicative of ESP as is high scoring. It would seem that in order to give the wrong answer the majority of times, it is necessary to know the correct answers. Thus those who scored far below chance were using their ESP to perceive what the correct answer was subconsciously, but for some reason they blocked out this answer and gave an incorrect one. Those achieving low scores do not realize what is happening. In fact they may think that they are doing their best.

Commander Mitchell and the researchers with whom he was working had accumulated some interesting statistics. Two of the four receivers had scored far above chance and two far below chance, tending to prove the existence of ESP. However, Commander Mitchell and his colleagues were being cautious. Their experiments, although interesting, could still not be declared as absolute proof. Scientists know that proof of any phenomenon can be established only after countless experiments covering a wide variety of different situations.

What then had Commander Mitchell's experiments accomplished? The single most important thing was to indicate to the world that serious research is being conducted in the area of ESP. Long regarded as a kind of novelty or parlor game, the experiments by Commander Mitchell, a highly trained scientist, elevated the position of a field that is still in its infancy. The experiments also brought to light the fact that future astronauts could possibly be trained in ESP and telepathy in particular. With man talking of future flights to Mars and further, it is not beyond the realm of possibility that telepathy will be the only means by which astronauts will be able to communicate in certain emergency situations.

Apollo 14 was a huge success and its accomplishments were a tribute to the courage and scientific knowledge of man. Yet perhaps someday the simple experiments in extrasensory perception conducted in outer space by Commander Edgar Mitchell may prove a landmark every bit as important as the moon landing. For Commander Mitchell was engaged in the pursuit of one of man's last frontiers, every bit as magnificent as the mysteries of outer space — the exploration of the mind of man.

BIBLIOGRAPHY

The Search for Atlantis

Atlantis, The Truth Behind the Legend by A. G. Galanopoulous and Edward Bacon. Indianapolis, Bobbs-Merrill, 1969

Atlantis; The Autobiography of a Search by Robert Ferro and Michael Grumley. Garden City, New York, Doubleday, 1970

Lost Atlantis; New Light on an Old Legend by J. V. Luce. New York, McGraw-Hill, 1969

Voyage to Atlantis by James W. Mavor, Jr. New York, Putnam, 1969

Bigfoot

A Modern Look at Monsters by Daniel Cohen. New York, Dodd, Mead and Company, 1970

This Baffling World by John Godwin. New York, Hart Publishing Company, 1968

On the Track of Unknown Animals by Bernard Heuvelmans. New York, Hill and Wang, 1965

Abominable Snowman: Legend Come to Life by Ivan Sanderson. Philadelphia, Chilton, 1961

Trail of the Abominable Snowman by Gardner Soule. New York, Putman, 1966

Visitors from the Skies

Behind the Flying Saucer Mystery by George Adamski. New York, Paperback Library, 1961

Flying Saucers Have Arrived by Bill Adler. New York, World Publishing Company, 1970

Final Report of the Scientific Study of Unidentified Flying Objects by Edward Condon. New York, Dutton, 1969

Flying Saucers, Here and Now! by Frank Edwards. New York, Bantam Books, 1966

Incident at Exeter by John Fuller. New York, Putnam, 1966

The Man Who Laughed at Death

Houdini; The Untold Story by Christopher Milbourne. New York, Crowell, 1969

Houdini; The Man Who Walked through Walls New York, Holt, Rinehart and Winston, 1957

The Great Houdini, Magician Extraordinary by Beryl Williams and Samuel Epstein. New York, Messner, 1950

Supernatural edited by Phil Hirsch. New York, Pyramid Publications Inc., 1968. See chapter 5, "The Strange Death of Harry Houdini"

The Strange Case of the Mary Celeste

Sea Fights and Shipwrecks by Hanson Baldwin. Garden City, New York, The Country Life Press, 1955

Posted Missing by Alan Villiers. New York, Charles Scribner's Sons, 1956

Famous Mysteries of the Sea by Patricia Lauber. New York, Thomas Nelson and Sons, 1962

The Loch Ness Monster—Fact or Fiction?

The Elusive Monster; An Analysis of the Evidence from Loch Ness by Maurice Burton. London, Hart-Davis, 1961

Loch Ness Monster by Tim Dinsdale. Philadelphia, Chilton, 1961

The Loch Ness Monster and Others by Rupert Thomas Gould. New York University Books, 1969

The Great Orm of Loch Ness by F. W. Holiday. New York, Norton, 1969

Lincoln's Dreams

True Experiences in Prophecy edited by Martin Ebon. New York, The New American Library, 1967

O Captain! by Leroy Hayman. New York, Four Winds Press, 1968

The Lost Patrol

Mysteries and Adventures along the Atlantic Coast by Edward Snow. Freeport, New York, Books for Libraries Press, 1969

Posted Missing by Alan Villiers. New York, Scribner's, 1956

Weird Unsolved Mysteries by Eric Norman. New York, Universal Publishing and Distributing Corporation, 1969

The Invasion of the Martians

The Invasion from Mars, A Study in the Psychology of Panic by Hadley Cantril. New York, Harper and Row, 1966

The Panic Broadcast; Portrait of an Event by Howard Koch. Boston, Little, Brown, 1970

Outer Space Experiments in ESP

ESP: Fact or Fancy by Dorothy Sara. New York, HC Publishers Inc., 1970

ESP and You by Hans Holzer. New York, Hawthorn Books, 1968

ESP in Life and Lab; Tracing Hidden Channels of the Mind by Louisa Rhine. New York, Macmillan, 1967

Your Mysterious Powers of ESP; the New Medium of Communication by Harold Sherman. New York, World Publishing Company, 1969

The Psychic Feats of Olaf Jonsson by Brad Steiger. Englewood Cliffs, N.J., Prentice Hall, 1971

The Unexplained by Allen Spraggett. New York, New American Library, 1967